QUALITY MANAGEMENT STANDARD FOR CIVIL WORKS

QUALITY MANAGEMENT STANDARD FOR CIVIL WORKS

MOTOR COLUMBUS Consulting Engineers Inc.
CH – 5400 Baden, Switzerland

SPIE BATIGNOLLES
33, Quai de Dion-Bouton
92814 Puteaux, France

SOCOTEC
Tour Maine-Montparnasse
33, Avenue du Maine
75755 Paris, France

MACMILLAN PRESS
LONDON

First published 1984 by
THE MACMILLAN PRESS LTD
London and Basingstoke
Companies and representatives
throughout the world

Filmset in 10/11pt Compugraphic Times by
CK Typesetters Ltd., Sutton, Surrey
Printed in Great Britain at
The Camelot Press Ltd, Southampton

ISBN 0 333 37067 8

Contents

Introduction	vi
QUALITY MANAGEMENT DIRECTIVE	1
QUALITY MANAGEMENT REQUIREMENTS D1 (for Design)	17
QUALITY MANAGEMENT REQUIREMENTS D2 (for Design)	33
QUALITY MANAGEMENT REQUIREMENTS D3 (for Design)	47
QUALITY MANAGEMENT REQUIREMENTS M1 (for Manufacturing)	51
QUALITY MANAGEMENT REQUIREMENTS M2A (for Manufacturing)	71
QUALITY MANAGEMENT REQUIREMENTS M2B (for Manufacturing)	89
QUALITY MANAGEMENT REQUIREMENTS M3 (for Manufacturing)	95
QUALITY MANAGEMENT REQUIREMENTS C1 (for Construction)	99
QUALITY MANAGEMENT REQUIREMENTS C2 (for Construction)	121
QUALITY MANAGEMENT REQUIREMENTS C3 (for Construction)	145

Introduction

'QUALITY MUST BE PRODUCED. IT CAN NEVER BE ACHIEVED BY VERIFICATION AND CHECKING ONLY'.

The evolution and growing complexity of techniques and technologies, together with the internationalization of contracts, have led to the use of technicians, materials and equipment from different origins. This and the increasing size of projects, have highlighted the necessity for a specific quality management system that is compatible with the needs of all the parties involved: owners, architects, engineers, contractors, suppliers and independent inspection agencies.

In view of this objective

— MOTOR COLUMBUS Consulting Engineers Inc.
— SPIE BATIGNOLLES
— SOCOTEC

have combined their efforts to develop a Quality Management Standard that can be applied to all kinds of civil works.

To facilitate implementation, the requirements have been established specifically for the following types of activity:

— Design
— Manufacturing
— Construction

This standard has also been structured in such a way as to provide compatibility with the following quality assurance standards and codes of practice:

— IAEA Code of Practice 50-C-QA
— Canadian Standard CSA Z299
— American Standard ANSI N45.2
— British Standard BS 5750

The authors are indebted to the Canadian Standards Association for permission to use CSA Z299 as a springboard for the ideas contained in this Standard.

Quality Management Directive

Contents

1.	OBJECTIVE	2
2.	CONCEPT AND BASIS	2
3.	CONTENTS OF APPLICABLE QUALITY MANAGEMENT REQUIREMENTS	4
4.	APPLICATION OF THE QUALITY MANAGEMENT DIRECTIVE AND THE QUALITY MANAGEMENT REQUIREMENTS	5
4.1.	General	5
4.2.	Guidelines for Selecting Quality Management Requirements. Examples	5
4.3.	Comments on Classification of Design Activities	7
4.4.	Comments on Classification of Manufacturing Activities	8
4.5.	Comments on Classification of Construction Activities	9
5.	DEFINITION OF TERMS	9
6.	COMPATIBILITY WITH OTHER STANDARDS	14

1. OBJECTIVE

This Quality Management Directive explains the structure of the Quality Management Standard and shows the relationships between its different Quality Management Requirements.

The aim of the Quality Management Standard for Civil Works is to assure QUALITY in civil works (design, manufacturing and construction) as required in accordance with the project contracts, through the setting-up of an appropriate system.

The Quality Management Standard is a quality management methodology that is independent of regulations, codes, standards, design criteria and technical specifications.

This standard is intended for use in civil works but its implementation may be extended to other disciplines. It can also be used in combination with other quality assurance standards.

2. CONCEPT AND BASIS

Quality assurance implies a system and methodology, the basis of which is defined in a standard stipulating the general requirements to be complied with by each organization participating in a project.

Based on these general requirements, specific documents have to be issued by each party for practical implementation.

The effectiveness of the implementation must then be verified.

The set-up of such a quality management system based on this Quality Management Standard is illustrated in the diagrammatic representation at the top of page 3.

The Quality Management Requirements are separate chapters of this standard that cover design, manufacturing and construction for each of three quality assurance levels.

Each of these chapters repeats the same pattern of basic and specific requirements, adapted to the activity and graded to suit each level of quality assurance.

The technical requirements for quality may be the same for the three levels but the methodology for management of this quality is graded from level 1 to 3. This is in order to establish the optimum way known to realize a work, in the environment where it has to be done, and to achieve the required results, at a given price.

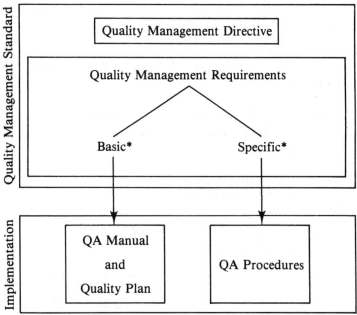

*Refer to table of section 3.

Therefore, quality assurance level 1 provides a methodology that is the most systematic, formalized, time consuming and costly. Level 2 combines the reasonably desirable with the practically feasible. Level 3 constitutes what is considered as good enough practice.

The structure of the Quality Management Requirements is shown in the following matrix:

		Design	Manufacturing	Construction
	1	D1	M1	C1
Quality Assurance Levels	2	D2	M2A M2B	C2
	3	D3	M3	C3

D1 to D3, M1 to M3 and C1 to C3 are the designations of the different Quality Management Requirements.

The contract shall specify the applicable Quality Management Requirements.

The contents of the different Quality Management Requirements are listed in section 3.

3. CONTENTS OF APPLICABLE QUALITY MANAGEMENT REQUIREMENTS

Key to symbols:

M   : Mandatory requirements.
O   : Optional requirements.
M/O: Requirements containing both clauses that are mandatory and clauses that are optional.
—   : Not applicable.
G   : Only as a guideline.

| | Graded Quality Management Requirements for Civil Works | | | | | | | | | |
| QUALITY MANAGEMENT REQUIREMENTS | Design | | | Manufacturing | | | | Construction | | |
	D1	D2	D3	M1	M2A	M2B	M3	C1	C2	C3
Basic Requirements:										
— Quality Assurance/ Inspection Programme	M	M	—	M	M	M	—	M	M	—
— Organization	M	M/O	—	M	M	M	—	M	M/O	—
— Quality Assurance Documents	M	M/O	—	M	M	M	—	M	M/O	—
Specific Requirements:										
— Design Management	M	M/O	M	—	—	—	—	—	—	—
— Document Control	M	M/O	M	M	M	—	—	M	M/O	—
— Procurement	M	M/O	M	M	M	—	—	M	M/O	M
— Measuring and Testing Equipment	—	—	—	M	M	M	M	M	M/O	M
— Inspection and Test	—	—	—	M	M	M	M	M	M	M
— In-process Inspection	—	—	—	M	M	—	—	M	M/O	—
— Final Inspection	—	—	—	M	M	—	—	M	M/O	—
— Inspection Status	—	—	—	M	M	—	—	M	M/O	—
— Identification & Traceability	—	—	—	M	M	—	—	M	O	—
— Preservation, Handling & Storage	—	—	—	M	G	—	—	M	O	—
— Manufacturing/ Construction	—	—	—	M	G	—	—	M	O	—
— Special Processes	—	—	—	M	M	—	—	M	O	—
— Packaging, Shipping	—	—	—	M	M	—	—	—	—	—
— Quality Records	M	M/O	M	M	M	M	M	M	M/O	M
— Non-conformance	—	—	—	M	M	M	M	M	M/O	M
— Customer-supplied Items	—	—	—	M	M	M	—	M	O	—
— Corrective Action	M	—	—	M	—	—	—	M	—	—
— Audits	M	—	—	M	—	—	—	M	—	—

4. APPLICATION OF THE QUALITY MANAGEMENT DIRECTIVE AND THE QUALITY MANAGEMENT REQUIREMENTS

4.1. GENERAL

Before quality can be verified, characteristics must be clearly defined in the design output documents. This is the only way to effectively produce, document and verify quality.

The quality assurance programme will provide only the means by which one can be sure that the specified activities are accomplished in a planned, systematic and documented manner, and in compliance with the specified requirements.

Specifying a quality assurance programme must not be considered as an alternative to full identification and specification of the quality characteristics in the design documentation. Further, a quality assurance programme does not replace the need to identify the required inspection, testing, manufacturing, construction and special processes.

4.2. GUIDELINES FOR SELECTING QUALITY MANAGEMENT REQUIREMENTS

All buildings, structures, items and services shall be classified to quality assurance levels 1, 2 or 3, for the respective activities of design D, manufacturing M, or construction C as described in the present conceptual part of the Quality Management Standard.

For such classification, the following factors must be taken into account:

— complexity of the activity, building, structure or item.
— maturity of technology.
— importance of malfunction (significance of failure).

A complex item can consist of simple elements and this shall be reflected by the selection of Quality Management Requirements. In other words, the complex item may be designed and constructed to quality assurance level 1 whereas the subitems, being simple elements, may be designed, manufactured and constructed according to quality assurance level 2 or 3.

Such a selection shall be in such a way that the overall quality is not impaired.

Example: Contract for a building with a relatively simple design but a complex construction method.

Design	Manufacturing	Construction
		C1 Structural works . . .
D2	M2B Reinforcing Structural steel Cements Aggregates	. . . . C3 Painting Drainage Waterproofing

It is important to know that the quality assurance classification of an item or service shall not depend on the selection of the subcontractors. In cases where a subcontractor cannot fulfil the requirements of an initial quality assurance classification (for example, the given Quality Management Requirements), a subcontract may be awarded on the basis of fewer requirements or clauses thereof, provided that the contractor makes up for these missing requirements.

Example: If the contract requires a separate design verification, it is questionable whether a small engineering company can assure it. In such a case, the subcontract may be awarded; however, the contractor shall take steps for the verification to be performed by an external organization.

This guide should be used by any party having to select the Quality Management Requirements appropriate to the design, supply, manufacturing or construction of an item or service. It has been developed for use in conjunction with the selected relevant Quality Management Requirements listed in this Quality Management Directive. Its use should ensure a uniform approach to classification and to selection of the Quality Management Requirements.

The Quality Management Requirements contain modulated requirements to allow for the elaboration of a quality assurance programme, including all provisions necessary to achieve the required degree of control, measurement and assurance for a very wide range of items and services. In all cases, the selected Quality Management Requirements shall contain the minimum requirements necessary to enable detection and correction of possible non-conformances that could occur during the performance of the activities specified by the purchase contract.

4.3. COMMENTS ON CLASSIFICATION OF DESIGN ACTIVITIES

D1, D2 or D3 shall apply for design activities and their procurement.

— Design complexity: this factor essentially relates to the difficulty of performing the design. It is the overall complexity of carrying out the design tasks and not the complexity of the items or their function.
— Maturity of technology: this factor defines the availability of proven design. The analysis should be based on market availability and the capability of prospective design offices and their subcontractors.
— Importance of malfunction: this factor should be considered in terms of failure probability and the consequences of such a failure should it occur.

D1 shall be selected if the design effort is extensive or complex and/or if the design is new from the first principles and/or if failure or malfunction could result in an undue risk to the health and safety of the operating personnel and the public.

D3 shall be selected if the design effort is minimal and simple, or if a proven design is available and if there is no risk to the health and safety of the operating personnel and the public.

For intermediate levels of complexity, maturity and importance of malfunction, D2 without or with optional requirements shall be selected.

4.4. COMMENTS ON CLASSIFICATION OF MANUFACTURING ACTIVITIES

— Manufacturing complexity: this factor accounts for the complexity of design, the reliability aspects of the item's function, the need for special controls over processes used in manufacturing, the degree to which the quality of the item can be directly verified by inspection or test, the attainment of standardization of materials used, manufacturing and testing processes and examination methods, the ease of replacement of parts after installation and conditions of access for in-service inspection.

— Maturity of technology: this factor accounts for proven manufactured items. The analysis should be based on market availability and the capability of prospective manufacturers and their subcontractors.

— Importance of malfunction: this factor should be considered in terms of failure probability and the consequence of such a failure should it occur.

M1 shall be selected if items or services require a large number of complex processes, if items have a large number of tight and interrelated characteristics, if the manufacturing process is new and/or if a malfunction could result in an undue risk to the health and safety of the operating personnel and the public.

M3 shall be selected if items or services require only a few simple processes or have no tight or interrelated characteristics, or if the technology is proven and if there is no risk to the health and safety of the operating personnel and the public should a failure or malfunction occur.

Intermediate levels shall be covered by M2A or M2B.

Owing to the more standardized nature of manufacturing activities (in relation to design and construction), two separate Quality Management Requirements containing only mandatory requirements are proposed for level 2.

4.5. COMMENTS ON CLASSIFICATION OF CONSTRUCTION ACTIVITIES

— Construction complexity: this factor accounts for the complexity of the systems, structures or parts thereof, the reliability aspects of their function, the need for special controls over processes used in construction, inspection and testing, the degree to which the structure quality can be directly verified by inspection or test, the attainment of standardization of materials used, construction and testing processes, the ease of replacement of parts after installation and condition of access for in-service inspection.
— Maturity of technology: the analysis should be based on market availability and the capability of prospective contractors and their subcontractors.
— Importance of malfunction: this factor should be considered in terms of failure probability and the consequences of such a failure should it occur.

C1 shall be selected if the structure or a major structural part is unusual or difficult to build and/or if the contractor has little experience in this field and/or if there is an undue risk to the health and safety of the operating personnel and the public should a failure occur.

C3 shall be selected if the construction process is simple, or if the contractor is experienced in this field and if there is no risk to the health and safety of the operating personnel and the public should a failure occur.

For intermediate levels, C2 without or with optional requirements shall be selected.

5. DEFINITION OF TERMS

The following definitions are provided to ensure a uniform understanding of selected terms related to quality management.

APPROVAL means an act of endorsing or adding positive authorization or both. Documents subject to approval will not be implemented until the approving party has signified his acceptance in writing.

AUDIT means a documented activity aimed at verifying by

examination and evaluation of objective evidence that the applicable elements of the Quality Assurance Programme have been established, effectively implemented and documented in compliance with specified requirements.

BATCH (or **LOT**) means an identifiable collection of items, or quantity of material, of a single type, grade, class, size or composition produced in the same plant, under essentially the same conditions and essentially at the same time.

CALIBRATION means the comparison of an item of measuring and test equipment with a reference standard or with another item of measuring and test equipment of equal or higher precision to detect and quantify inaccuracies and to report or eliminate these inaccuracies.

CHARACTERISTIC means any distinct property or attribute of an item, process or service that can be described and measured to determine conformance or non-conformance to specified requirements.

COMPONENT means a limitable part of a system.

CONCURRENCE means an act of endorsing based on mutual consent of the two parties. Documents submitted for concurrence may be implemented immediately at the issuing party's discretion.

CONSTRUCTION (**C**) means erection, installation, fabrication, assembling, testing and commissioning of items involving civil and also mechanical and electrical works, at the permanent site of the facility or plant, by the party performing the work.

CONTRACT means the written covenant and other documents agreed to and legally binding between the customer and contractor, which specify requirements and conditions that must be complied with to complete the work satisfactorily.

CONTRACTOR means owner, architect, engineer, consultant, manufacturer, erector, installer, or whoever performs or contracts to perform any work either for his own use or for that of another and for or without remuneration.

CORRECTIVE ACTION means the set of actions necessary to determine the cause of non-conformances and to take steps to prevent recurrence.

CUSTOMER means the party or his representative issuing a contract for procuring items and services.

DESIGN (D) means the technical and management processes that commence with the identification of design input and that lead to and include the issuance of design output documents.

DESIGN INPUT means those criteria, parameters,

assumptions or other design requirements upon which detailed final design is based.

DESIGN OUTPUT means drawings, specifications and other documents that define technical requirements for structures, systems and components.

DESIGN REVIEW means critical examination and evaluation to provide assurance that design documents are correct and satisfactory.

EVALUATION means an appraisal to determine whether manufacturing and construction processes and quality programmes are capable of producing an item or service of the specified quality and of generating evidence that supports decisions of acceptability.

EXAMINATION means an element of inspection consisting of investigation of materials, components, supplies or services to determine conformance to those specified requirements that can be determined by such investigation. Examination is usually non-destructive and includes, but is not limited to, simple physical manipulation, gauging and measurement.

GUIDELINES mean particular provisions in the programme, which are considered good practice but which are not mandatory, that are intended to comply with this Standard.

HIERARCHICAL DESIGN VERIFICATION means verification performed by the direct supervisor of those who did the original design.

INSPECTION means any or all of the careful examination, measurement and testing of the characteristics of items and services to determine whether they meet contractual requirements.

INTERFACE means a boundary, within the same task, at which the activities necessary for the completion of the task are performed by two or several organizations or departments of the same organization. The identification of an interface includes the definition of the relationship between participating organizations.

ITEM means raw material, part, component, subassembly, assembly, equipment, subsystem, system, structure or finished product.

MANUFACTURING (M) means the production and supply, fabrication, or assembly of items on the premises of the party performing the work.

MONITORING PROCESS means physical attendance at the performance of an activity to ascertain by verification or observation that all the parameters of the required processes are maintained within the specifications as defined by the process procedures.

NON-CONFORMANCE means a deficiency in a characteristic, documentation or procedure that renders the quality of an item or service unacceptable or indeterminate, until a proper resolution has been done. Examples of non-conformance include: physical defects, test failures, incorrect or inadequate documentation or deviations from prescribed processing and inspection or test procedures.

OBJECTIVE EVIDENCE means any statement of fact, information, or record, either quantitative or qualitative, pertaining to the quality of an item or service based on observations, measurements or tests that can be verified.

OWNER means the party who will have title to the item being manufactured or the facility or installation under construction.

POSITIVE RECALL means a situation where an item is released, so that further work can proceed, provided that the item can be removed or repaired if found unacceptable at a later stage.

PROCEDURE means a document that states the purpose and scope of an activity and specifies how to perform it. In general, procedures shall be established by the personnel or organization performing the relevant work. Procedures may include check-lists.

PROCUREMENT means all those activities necessary for acquiring items or services from other sources. Procurement includes the translation of the requirements from design output documents into procurement specifications and orders, subcontractor's evaluation, selection, surveillance, manufacture control and receiving inspection.

QUALITY means the aptitude of an item or service to qualify for the intended need.

QUALITY ASSURANCE (QA) means a planned or systematic pattern of all means and actions necessary to provide adequate confidence that items or services meet the intended need.

QUALITY ASSURANCE DOCUMENTATION means the QA manual, quality plans when applicable, and/or QA procedures.

QUALITY ASSURANCE PROGRAMME means the programme as prepared by the contractor in accordance with the Quality Management Requirements. It is described in the QA manual.

QUALITY ASSURANCE REPRESENTATIVE (QAR) means the competent person appointed by the customer to survey and assess the quality of the contractor's work.

QUALITY CONTROL (QC) means those actions that provide a means to measure and regulate the characteristics of an item or service to established requirements.

QUALITY MANAGEMENT DIRECTIVE is the conceptual part of the Quality Management Standard for Civil Works that describes the methodology and provides general guidelines for the civil quality management system and its set-up.

QUALITY MANAGEMENT REQUIREMENTS are the separate sections of the Quality Management Standard for Civil Works that contain the Basic and Specific Requirements to be complied with for each quality assurance level 1, 2 and 3 of the three activities design, D, manufacturing, M, and construction, C.

QUALITY MANAGEMENT STANDARD FOR CIVIL WORKS is the document that consists of the Quality Management Directive and the Quality Management Requirements.

REPAIR means reprocessing a non-conforming item so that it can function reliably and safely even though the item still does not conform to the originally specified requirements.

REWORK means reprocessing an item to conform to the originally specified requirements.

SERVICE means work and incidental material as specified in a contract such as inspection, non-destructive examination, calibration, testing, welding, analysis, etc.

SPECIAL PROCESS means a manufacturing activity in which the end results cannot be totally evaluated without performing a destructive test. There are, however, definable parameters which, if controlled within the specified range, provide a high probability that the product would be acceptable if fully tested.

SUBCONTRACTOR means the party to whom a contract has been awarded by a contractor.

SURVEILLANCE means the evaluation and analysis of records, methods, procedures, items and services, including verification, to assure that requirements are met.

SYSTEM means part of the plant consisting of components combined to a functional installation.

6. COMPATIBILITY WITH OTHER STANDARDS

QUALITY MANAGEMENT REQUIREMENT LEVEL 1	IAEA CODE OF PRACTICE 50-C-QA	CANADIAN STANDARD CSA Z299.1	AMERICAN STANDARD ANSI N45.2	BRITISH STANDARD BS 5750 PART 1
BASIC REQUIREMENTS				
QA Programme	QA Programmes	QA Programme	QA Programme	Quality System/ Planning/Training
Organization	Organization	Organization	Organization	Organization
QA Documents:		Quality Programme Documents		
— QA Manual	QA Programmes	Manual	QA Programme	Quality System
— Quality Plan	Inspection & Test Control	Inspection and Test Plan	Inspection & Test Control	Planning/Sampling Procedure
— QA Procedures	QA Programmes	System Function Procedures	Instructions, Procedures & Drawings	Work Instructions
SPECIFIC REQUIREMENTS		*SYSTEM FUNCTIONS*		
Design Management	Design Control	Contract Review	Design Control	Design Control
Document Control	Document Control	Design Assurance Document Control	Document Control	Documentation & Changes Control
Procurement	Procurement Control	Purchasing/Incoming Inspection	Procurement Document Control/Control of Purchased Material, Equipment & Services	Control of Purchased Material & Services

Measuring & Testing Equipment	Inspection & Test Control	Measuring & Testing Equipment	Control of Measuring & Test Equipment	Control of Inspection, Measuring & Test Equipment
Inspection & Test/In-process Inspection/Final Inspection	Inspection & Test Control	In-process Inspection/Final Inspection	Inspection/Test Control	Manufacturing Control
Inspection Status	Inspection & Test Control	Inspection Status	Inspection, Test & Operating Status	Indication of Inspection Status Records
Identification & Traceability	Material Control	Identification & Traceability	Identification & Control of Materials, Parts & Components	
Preservation, Handling & Storage	Material Control	Handling & Storing	Handling, Storage & Shipping	Protection & Preservation of Product Quality
Manufacturing/Construction	Process Control	Manufacturing & Construction	Instructions, Procedures & Drawings	Manufacturing Control
Special Processes	Process Control	Special Processes	Control of Special Processes	Manufacturing Control
Packaging & Shipping	Material Control	Preservation, Packaging & Shipping	Handling, Storage & Shipping	Protection & Preservation of Product Quality
Quality Records Non-conformances	Records Non-conformance Control	Quality Records Non-conformance	QA Records Non-conforming Items	Records Control of Non-conforming Material
Customer-supplied Items	Not Covered	Customer-supplied Items	Not Covered	Purchaser-supplied Material
Corrective Action Audits	Corrective Action Audits	Corrective Action Audits	Corrective Action Audits	Corrective Action Review of Quality System

Quality Management Requirements D1

Contents

1.	SCOPE	19
1.1.	General	19
1.2.	Applicability	19
1.3.	Contractor's Responsibilities	19
2.	DEFINITIONS	20
3.	REQUIREMENTS	20
3.1.	Basic Requirements	20
3.1.1.	Quality Assurance Programme	20
3.1.2.	Organization	20
3.1.3.	Quality Assurance Documents	21
3.1.3.1.	Quality Assurance Manual	21
3.1.3.2.	Quality Assurance Procedures	22
3.2.	Specific Requirements	22
3.2.1.	Design Management	22
3.2.1.1.	Design Planning	22
3.2.1.2.	Design Input Requirements	23
3.2.1.3.	Design Process	23
3.2.1.4.	Interface Control	24
3.2.1.5.	Design Verification	25
3.2.1.6.	Design Changes	25
3.2.1.7.	Computer Programs	26
3.2.2.	Document Control	26
3.2.3.	Procurement of Design Activities	27
3.2.3.1.	Selection of Subcontractors	27
3.2.3.2.	Subcontract Requirements	27
3.2.3.3.	Amendments to Subcontracts	28
3.2.3.4.	Verification of the Quality Management System Implemented by a Subcontractor	28
3.2.4.	Quality Records	28

3.2.5. Corrective Action   29
3.2.6. Audits   29

4.   VERIFICATION OF QUALITY   30

4.1. Initial Evaluation of Quality Assurance
       Programme and Physical Resources   30
4.2. Continuing Evaluation and Verification   31
4.3. Access   31

1. SCOPE

1.1. GENERAL

This chapter specifies requirements to be incorporated in a contractor's quality assurance programme for design. The contractor is responsible for planning and developing a programme that assures that all his management, design and technical responsibilities for quality are incorporated and executed effectively. The programme is aimed primarily at ensuring an efficient quality management in design and at taking corrective actions, when necessary.

Planning and detailed written procedures are essential for specifying how such activities as the following, which affect quality, are to be performed and controlled:

(a) Design management.
(b) Procurement.
(c) Documentation and quality records.
(d) Corrective action to prevent recurrence of design deficiencies.
(e) Quality audits and management reviews.

1.2. APPLICABILITY

The requirements of this chapter apply to the design activities when specified in a contract.

1.3. CONTRACTOR'S RESPONSIBILITIES

The contractor's responsibilities are:

(a) To develop and implement the controls and quality assurance procedures, specified herein, that will promptly detect and correct, or prevent, non-conformances to technical requirements.
(b) To comply with the customer's requirements as specified in the contract.
(c) To prepare a quality assurance manual which shall be submitted to the customer for concurrence before the contract is awarded or at the latest before the work starts, as required in 3.1.3.1.

(d) To update and resubmit the quality assurance manual to reflect current practices when significant changes occur in the contractor's programme or organization in order to improve its effectiveness or to prevent recurrence of design deficiencies.

(e) To initiate corrective measures promptly when the quality assurance representative notifies the contractor of deviations from established requirements.

2. DEFINITIONS

Refer to Quality Management Directive.

3. REQUIREMENTS

3.1. BASIC REQUIREMENTS

3.1.1. *Quality Assurance Programme*

The contractor shall plan, establish, implement, and maintain a quality assurance programme that complies with the requirements of this chapter.

3.1.2. *Organization*

The contractor shall:

(a) Clearly define management policies, objectives and responsibilities for quality assurance, including the responsibility of each division within a multi-divisional organization. The responsibility and authority for quality of those managing and performing the design and of those auditing and verifying conformance to quality requirements shall be defined and their relationships shown on organization charts.

(b) Provide for the review by management of the status and adequacy of the quality assurance programme.

(c) Appoint a representative, who shall report regularly to management at a level that ensures that quality assurance requirements are not subordinated to design, and define his authority to resolve quality matters. The customer shall be notified of the appointment in writing.

(d) Define the responsibility and authority of personnel who are primarily responsible for quality assurance and their organizational independence during audits and define the responsibility and authority of personnel who are primarily responsible for design control (including design verifiers) and their organizational independence to:

 (i) identify and record quality problems
 (ii) initiate or recommend or provide solutions through designated channels
 (iii) verify the implementation of dispositions.

Note that, generally, audit personnel shall not be involved directly in the specific project design work.

3.1.3. Quality Assurance Documents

3.1.3.1. Quality Assurance Manual
(a) The contractor shall:

 (i) Prepare a quality assurance manual, approved and signed by a senior management official and submit it for the customer's concurrence before the contract is awarded or at the latest before the work starts. A quality assurance manual submitted under a previous contract or tender may be referred to.
 (ii) Review and update the manual to reflect current quality assurance policies and procedures and resubmit the resulting manual.
 (iii) Implement the programme according to the provisions specified in the manual.

(b) The quality assurance manual shall deal as appropriate with the following:

 (i) Organization — The manual shall define the organizational measures as specified in 3.1.2.
 (ii) Quality assurance procedures — Documented QA procedures as specified in 3.1.3.2. shall

be included or shall be outlined and cross-referenced. Referenced QA procedures shall be made available to the quality assurance representative.

(iii)   Manual review — A statement shall be incorporated for reviewing and updating the manual as specified in 3.1.3.1.(a)(ii).

3.1.3.2.   *Quality Assurance Procedures*

The contractor shall have procedures for the following specific requirements should they apply to the contract:

Design management	Clause 3.2.1.
Document control	Clause 3.2.2.
Procurement of design activities	Clause 3.2.3.
Quality records	Clause 3.2.4.
Corrective action	Clause 3.2.5.
Audits	Clause 3.2.6.

For design management, procedures or standard forms are necessary only if they are specifically required in the subclauses of 3.2.1.

Each QA procedure shall define, as applicable, such things as: its purpose and scope; who is responsible for what; how, when and where all steps are to be performed; what materials, equipment, and documentation are to be used; how it is all controlled.

Forms used shall be exhibited.

QA procedures shall be updated when necessary.

3.2.   SPECIFIC REQUIREMENTS

3.2.1.   *Design Management*

3.2.1.1.   *Design Planning*

(a)   The design shall be planned.

(b)   Prior to the preparation of the design documents, the design input must be elaborated to suit the execution of works.

(c)   A general (preliminary) design shall be done for unusual structures or structures that have many interfaces, prior to the preparation of the detailed design.

3.2.1.2. Design Input Requirements
- (a) Design input shall be identified and transmitted in written form and the responsibility shall therefore be defined.
- (b) Design input shall be reviewed and agreed by the interfacing organizations.
- (c) Design input shall include:

  — Codes and standards (including deviations).
  — Basic functions of structures and buildings.
  — Design criteria (loads, load combinations including construction load combinations, environmental conditions, site data, fire-resistance criteria, deformation criteria).
  — Arrangement and layout drawings (guide drawings).
  — General technical data.

- (d) Incomplete, ambiguous or conflicting requirements shall be resolved and agreed by the organizations responsible for generation of the requirements.

3.2.1.3. Design Process
- (a) The preliminary design, if required in accordance with 3.2.1.1.(c), shall be done in such a way that all problems related to interactions (structures, equipment) can be resolved and that major dimensions of the buildings or structures can be selected.
- (b) For the preliminary design, the design input may be issued as a preliminary version.
- (c) Prior to the detailed design, the design input documents shall be agreed by interfacing organizations.
- (d) Design analysis (calculations), drawings, specifications or other design documents shall be prepared in accordance with procedures or standard-type documents. Measures shall be established to provide for the standardization of:

- formats
- identification of documents
- symbols
- status and revisions
- issuance and distribution
- reference documents
- storage and control of originals or master copies
- review and approval.

(e) For design analysis, measures shall be established to provide for:

- documentation of results of bibliographic investigations
- documentation of assumptions and design input
- identification of computer calculations.

(f) Design documents shall specify important construction methods and data, such as:

- special treatments
- sequence of operations
- applicable specifications
- special equipment
- work methods.

The respective responsibilities of the design office and the construction site organization for their preparation shall be clearly established.

(g) A procedure is required for 3.2.1.3.

3.2.1.4. *Interface Control*

(a) The interfaces between organizations performing activities that affect the quality of design shall be identified in writing.

(b) Design information transmitted from one organization to another shall be documented and identified. This flow of information shall be standardized by standard sheets or by procedures.

(c) Where it is necessary initially to forward design information verbally or by other informal means, the information shall be confirmed promptly in writing.

(d) A procedure is required for 3.2.1.4.

3.2.1.5.   *Design Verification*

  (a)   Design verifications shall be performed by competent personnel other than those who performed the initial design. This may be done by an external group or another group from the same organization.

  (b)   Calculations, specifications, design (conception) drawings and concepts of detailed drawings shall be subject to such a verification.

  (c)   Detailed drawings shall be subject to at least a hierarchical verification.

  (d)   Methods:

    (i)   Design verification shall include:

       — design review including computer program qualification as required by 3.2.1.7. or
       — alternative calculations or
       — qualification testing or
       — any combination thereof.

    (ii)   The verification shall bear on:

       — the selection of the input
       — the assumptions
       — the stability
       — the results
       — the serviceability
       — the conformity of design documents to procedures or standard-type documents.

  (e)   Design verification shall be documented in sufficient details (identification of verification and verification method) to allow for surveillance and audit.

  (f)   A procedure is required for 3.2.1.5.

3.2.1.6.   *Design Changes*

  (a)   Design changes that affect construction documents shall be in writing.

  (b)   They shall be prepared, reviewed and approved by the same organizations that prepared, reviewed and approved the initial documents or by organizations having an acceptable level of responsibility, authority and information.

  (c)   Design changes shall be identified, indexed and filed

for easy retrieval.
(d)   A design change procedure is required for 3.2.1.6.

3.2.1.7.   *Computer Programs*

(a)   Sophisticated computer programs shall be qualified and the qualification documented.

The qualification can be done by one of the following methods:

— verification by alternative calculations
— significant test calculations
— reference to previous qualifications
— independent verification of the algorithms.

3.2.2.   *Document Control*

The contractor shall:

(a)   Establish measures to ensure that all essential quality related documents, including but not limited to those listed below, are reviewed for adequacy and approved for release by authorized personnel:

(i)   Quality assurance manual required by 3.1.3.1.
(ii)   Quality assurance procedures required by 3.1.3.2.
(iii)   Design documents required by 3.2.1.
(iv)   Procurement documents required by 3.2.3.

(b)   Establish distribution lists for the above-mentioned documents, update them and maintain them in the current form to assure that the relevant personnel are issued with all the documents necessary to perform the activity concerned.

(c)   Make the applicable issues of these documents available at areas where these activities are performed.

(d)   Establish and update lists of applicable documents and distribute them systematically. Controlled distribution is required for these lists only.

(e)   Changes:

(i)   Refer to 3.2.1.6. for design changes.
(ii)   Maintain a record of changes as they are made. Written notes on documents are acceptable provided that they are made by authorized

persons according to established procedures. Documents shall be revised and re-issued after a practical number of changes have been issued.

3.2.3. Procurement of Design Activities

3.2.3.1. Selection of Subcontractors
The contractor shall identify design activities to be subcontracted.

He shall undertake the following:

(a) Determine for these subcontracted design activities the applicable Quality Management Requirements. Classification to these Quality Management Requirements shall be established in such a way that the overall quality of the design is not impaired. The classification list shall be submitted to the customer for acceptance.
(b) Evaluate and select subcontractors in accordance with 4.1. of the applicable Quality Management Requirements with regard to their experience, the qualification of the available personnel and the qualification of their computer programs.
(c) Document the selection of the subcontractor.

3.2.3.2. Subcontract Requirements
The contractor shall include the following in subcontracts as applicable:

(a) A clear description of the design activities to be procured including technical requirements by reference to codes, standards, design criteria, etc.
(b) A designation of the Quality Management Requirements to be applied to the activities and exceptions, if any.
(c) A designation of the contractor's QA procedures to be implemented by the subcontractor, if applicable.
(d) Instructions for the submission, retention and disposition of quality records.
(e) A statement related to the right of access to the subcontractor's premises and records for audit and/or surveillance by the contractor or the customer.

Subcontract documents shall be reviewed and approved in accordance with 3.2.2.(a). All unpriced subcontracts and associated reference data shall be available on request for review by the quality assurance representative.

3.2.3.3. *Amendments to Subcontracts*
The contractor shall process amendments to subcontracts in the same way as the initial subcontract and reference the initial subcontract number in amendments.

3.2.3.4. *Verification of the Quality Management System Implemented by a Subcontractor*
Refer to 4.2. of the applicable Quality Management Requirements.

3.2.4. *Quality Records*

The contractor shall:

(a) Maintain quality records as evidence that:

   (i)   The quality assurance programme meets the requirements of these Quality Management Requirements (manual, procedures).
   (ii) The design meets contractual requirements (drawings, specifications, calculations).
   (iii) The procurement of design activities meets the requirements of 3.2.3.
   (iv) Corrective action is being taken and is effective as required by 3.2.5.

(b) Include in (a) above quality audit records that identify:

   (i)   Quality assurance procedures, design and verification of the activities audited.
   (ii) Audit results.
   (iii) Analysis of audit data and evaluation of corrective action.

(c) Include in (a) above documents that identify the results of the design verifications.
(d) Identify, index, and file quality records for easy

retrieval.

(e) Retain quality records for the time specified in the contract (if not specified, they shall be retained for 10 years).

(f) Provide a suitable environment for storing of records to minimize deterioration or damage and to prevent loss (the use of a double filing system is an acceptable method).

3.2.5. Corrective Action

(a) Deficiencies or errors in the design may be detected through:

    (i) design verification
    (ii) current use of the design document
    (iii) audits
    (iv) tests
    (v) failure during operation
    (vi) other means.

(b) Design deficiencies shall be corrected in accordance with the existing procedures (for design verification, design change).

(c) In addition to correcting deficiencies in the design, the contractor shall investigate the cause of significant or recurring deficiencies and take appropriate action to prevent repetition.

(d) A procedure shall be prepared for providing such corrective action. This procedure shall enable the design verifier to initiate corrective action and contain provisions for reporting deficiencies and corrective action to an appropriate level of the contractor's management.

3.2.6. Audits

(a) The contractor shall establish, implement and document a plan for audits that objectively evaluates and verifies that:

    (i) He is complying with all aspects of his quality assurance programme, documented procedures and specified requirements.
    (ii) The quality assurance programme is

performing adequately.
- (iii) Recommended corrective actions are being implemented effectively.
- (iv) Deficient areas are being re-audited.

(b) The audit programme shall define:

- (i) Functional areas to be audited.
- (ii) Assignments of those performing the audits.
- (iii) Frequency of audits.
- (iv) Methods for reporting findings and recommendations.
- (v) The means for having corrective actions initiated and implemented.

(c) Audits shall include an evaluation of:

- (i) Design activities.
- (ii) Quality assurance practices, documented quality assurance procedures and instructions.
- (iii) Documents and records.

(d) Appropriately trained and qualified personnel, who are not directly responsible for the area being audited, shall perform the audits according to documented audit procedures or check-lists which shall identify the essential characteristics to be complied with. Auditors shall be cognizant in the field being audited.

(e) The management responsible for the area audited shall review and correct deficiencies identified in the documented audit results.

(f) If the design verification is performed by an external group, auditing of the design activities may be limited to auditing of the verification activities.

4. VERIFICATION OF QUALITY

4.1. INITIAL EVALUATION OF QUALITY ASSURANCE PROGRAMME AND PHYSICAL RESOURCES

Prior to the award of a contract for performance of the activity, the customer shall evaluate the contractor's quality assurance programme and resources to determine whether the requirements of this section can be met.

In the event of the prospective contractor not fulfilling all applicable requirements, the customer may award the contract provided that he takes the responsibility for those QA requirements that cannot be complied with by the contractor. In such a case the exception shall be clearly defined in the contract.

4.2.   CONTINUING EVALUATION AND VERIFICATION

The schedule and/or frequency of customer's and authorities' audits and surveillance should be outlined in the contract.

If not otherwise specified in the contract, a maximum of one audit and three surveillances will be performed each year.

4.3.   ACCESS

The contractor shall provide for reasonable access of the competent authorities and of the customer to his premises and records for audit and surveillance purposes.

Quality Management Requirements D2

Contents

1.	SCOPE	35
1.1.	General	35
1.2.	Applicability	35
1.3.	Contractor's Responsibilities	35
2.	DEFINITIONS	36
3.	REQUIREMENTS	36
3.1.	Basic Requirements	36
3.1.1.	Quality Assurance Programme	36
3.1.2.	Organization	36
3.1.3.	Quality Assurance Documents	37
3.1.3.1.	Quality Assurance Manual	37
3.1.3.2.	Quality Assurance Procedures	37
3.2.	Specific Requirements	38
3.2.1.	Design Management	38
3.2.1.1.	Design Input Requirements	38
3.2.1.2.	Design Process	38
3.2.1.3.	Interface Control	38
3.2.1.4.	Design Verification	39
3.2.1.5.	Design Changes	40
3.2.1.6.	Computer Programs	40
3.2.2.	Document Control	40
3.2.3.	Procurement of Design Activities	40
3.2.3.1.	Selection of Subcontractors	40
3.2.3.2.	Subcontract Requirements	41
3.2.3.3.	Amendments to Subcontracts	41
3.2.3.4.	Verification of the Quality Management System Implemented by a Subcontractor	41
3.2.4.	Quality Records	41
4.	VERIFICATION OF QUALITY	42

4.1. Initial Evaluation of Quality Assurance
      Programme, and Physical Resources   42
4.2. Continuing Evaluation and Verification   42
4.3. Access   43

5. ATTACHMENT: SUMMARY OF THE
    REQUIREMENTS   43

1. SCOPE

1.1. GENERAL

This chapter specifies requirements to be incorporated in a contractor's quality assurance programme for design. The contractor is responsible for planning and developing a programme that assures that all his management, design and technical responsibilities for quality are incorporated and executed effectively. The programme is aimed primarily at ensuring an efficient quality management in design.

Planning and detailed written procedures may be established for specifying how such activities as the following, which affect quality, are to be performed and controlled:

(a) Design management.
(b) Procurement.
(c) Documentation and quality records.

1.2. APPLICABILITY

The requirements of this section apply to the design activities when specified in a contract.

The mandatory requirements (identified as M in the left-hand margin) are always applicable if the contractual documents make reference to this chapter D2.

In addition to these mandatory requirements, optional requirements (identified as O in the left-hand margin) will be applicable if specifically addressed in the contractual documents.

1.3. CONTRACTOR'S RESPONSIBILITIES

The contractor's responsibilities are:

(a) To develop and implement the controls and quality assurance procedures specified herein.
(b) To comply with the customer's requirements as specified in the contract.
(c) To prepare a quality assurance manual which shall be submitted to the customer at the latest before the work starts, as required in 3.1.3.1.
(d) To update and resubmit the quality assurance manual

to reflect current practices when significant changes occur in the contractor's programme or organization in order to improve its effectiveness.

(e)   To initiate corrective measures promptly when the quality assurance representative notifies the contractor of deviations from established requirements.

2. DEFINITIONS

Refer to Quality Management Directive.

3. REQUIREMENTS

3.1. BASIC REQUIREMENTS

3.1.1. *Quality Assurance Programme*

M   The contractor shall plan, establish, implement and maintain a quality assurance programme that complies with the requirements of this chapter.

3.1.2. *Organization*

The contractor shall:

M   (a)   Appoint a representative who shall be responsible for quality assurance requirements and define his authority to resolve quality matters.

O   (b)   Clearly define management policies, objectives and responsibilities for quality assurance including the responsibility of each division within a multi-divisional organization. The responsibility and authority for quality of those managing and performing the design and of those verifying conformance to quality requirements shall be defined and their relationships shown on organization charts. The representative mentioned in (a) shall report regularly to management at a level that ensures that quality assurance requirements are not subordinated to design.

3.1.3. Quality Assurance Documents

3.1.3.1. Quality Assurance Manual
O   (a)   The contractor shall:

          (i)   Prepare a quality assurance manual, approved and signed by a senior management official and submit it for the customer's concurrence before the contract is awarded or at the latest before the work starts. A quality assurance manual submitted under a previous contract or tender may be referred to.

          (ii)   Review and update the manual to reflect current quality assurance policies and procedures and resubmit the resulting manual.

          (iii)   Implement the programme according to the provisions specified in the manual.

O   (b)   The quality assurance manual shall deal as appropriate with the following:

          (i)   Organization — The manual shall define the organizational measures as specified in 3.1.2.

          (ii)   Quality assurance procedures — Documented QA procedures as specified in 3.1.3.2. shall be included or shall be outlined and cross-referenced. Referenced QA procedures shall be made available to the quality assurance representative.

          (iii)   Manual review — A statement shall be incorporated for reviewing and updating the manual as specified in 3.1.3.1.(a)(ii).

3.1.3.2. Quality Assurance Procedures
M   The contractor shall have procedures for the following specific requirements if required in the corresponding clauses:

Design management	3.2.1.
Document control	3.2.2.
Procurement of design activities	3.2.3.
Quality records	3.2.4.

QA procedures shall be updated when necessary.

3.2. SPECIFIC REQUIREMENTS

3.2.1. *Design Management*

3.2.1.1. *Design Input Requirements*
Design input shall include, as applicable:

— Codes and standards (including deviations).
— Basic functions of structures and buildings.
— Design criteria (loads, load combinations including construction load combinations, environmental conditions, site data, fire-resistance criteria, deformation criteria).
— Arrangement and layout drawings (guide drawings).
— General technical data.

M   (a)   Prior to the preparation of design documents design input shall be identified and transmitted in written form.
M   (b)   Design input shall be reviewed and agreed by interfacing organizations.

3.2.1.2. *Design Process*
M   (a)   Design analysis (calculations), drawings, specifications or other design documents shall be established in accordance with procedures or standard-type documents.
M   (b)   For design analysis, requirements shall be established for:

— documentation of assumptions and design input
— identification of computer calculations.

M   (c)   Design documents shall specify important construction methods and data, such as:

— special treatments
— sequence of operations
— applicable specifications
— special equipment
— work methods.

3.2.1.3. *Interface Control*
M   (a)   The interfaces between organizations performing

activities that affect the quality of design shall be identified in writing.

O   (b)   Design information transmitted from one organization to another shall be documented and identified.

             Where it is necessary to initially forward design information verbally or by other informal means, the information shall be confirmed promptly in writing.

O   (c)   A procedure is required for 3.2.1.3.

3.2.1.4.   *Design Verification*
Design verification may be:

— design review including computer program qualification as required by 3.2.1.6. or
— alternative calculations or
— qualification testing or
— any combination thereof.

M   (a)   Design calculations, specifications, design (conception) drawings and concepts of detailed drawings shall be subject to a verification performed by a competent person other than the one who performed the initial design. Verification of design calculations may be performed by the same person who did the initial calculation provided that a different calculation method is used.

O   (b)   The verification shall bear on:

— the selection of the input
— the assumptions
— the stability
— the results
— the serviceability
— the conformity of design documents to procedures or standard-type documents.

O   (c)   Design verification shall be documented (identification of verifications and verification method) to permit surveillance.

O   (d)   A procedure is required for 3.2.1.4.(b) and (c).

3.2.1.5. Design Changes

M   (a)   Design changes that affect construction documents shall be in writing.

O   (b)   Design changes shall be identified and indexed for easy retrieval.

O   (c)   A design change procedure is required for 3.2.1.5.

3.2.1.6. Computer Programs

M   (a)   Sophisticated computer programs shall be qualified and the qualification documented.
       The qualification can be done by one of the following methods:

— verification by alternative calculations
— significant test calculations
— reference to previous qualifications
— independent verification of the algorithms.

3.2.2. Document Control

The contractor shall:

M   (a)   Establish measures to ensure that all essential quality related documents, including but not limited to those listed below, are approved for release:

(i)   Quality assurance manual required by 3.1.3.1.
(ii)   Quality assurance procedures required by 3.1.3.2.
(iii)   Design documents required by 3.2.1.
(iv)   Procurement documents required by 3.2.3.

O   (b)   Establish and update lists of applicable documents and distribute them systematically.

3.2.3. Procurement of Design Activities

3.2.3.1. Selection of Subcontractors
The contractor shall identify design activities to be subcontracted.
       He shall undertake the following:

M   (a)   Determine for these subcontracted design activities the applicable Quality Management Requirements.
       Classification to these Quality Management

Requirements shall be established in such a way that the overall quality of the design is not impaired. The classification list shall be submitted to the customer for acceptance.

O   (b)   Evaluate and select subcontractors in accordance with 4.1. of this chapter, if applicable, with regard to their experience, the qualification of the available personnel and the qualification of their computer programs.

3.2.3.2.   *Subcontract Requirements*
The contractor shall include the following in subcontracts as applicable:

M   (a)   A clear description of the design activities to be procured including technical requirements by reference to codes, standards, design criteria, etc.

M   (b)   A designation of the Quality Management Requirements to be applied to the activities and exceptions, if any.

M   (c)   A designation of the contractor's QA procedures to be implemented by the subcontractor, if applicable.

O   (d)   Instructions for the submission, retention and disposition of quality records.

O   (e)   A statement related to the right of access to the subcontractor's premises and records for surveillance by the contractor or the customer.

O   (f)   All unpriced subcontracts and associated reference data shall be available on request for review by the quality assurance representative.

M   (g)   Subcontract documents shall be approved in accordance with 3.2.2.(a).

3.2.3.3.   *Amendments to Subcontracts*
M   The contractor shall process amendments to subcontracts in the same way as the initial subcontract and reference the initial subcontract number in amendments.

3.2.3.4.   *Verification of the Quality Management System Implemented by a Subcontractor*
Refer to 4.2. of this chapter, if applicable.

3.2.4.   *Quality Records*

The contractor shall:

M   (a) Maintain quality records as evidence that the design meets the contractual requirements (drawings, specifications, calculations).
O   (b) Maintain quality records as evidence that:

    (i)   The quality assurance programme meets the requirements of these Quality Management Requirements (manual, procedures).
    (ii) The procurement of design activities meets the requirements of 3.2.3.

O   (c) Include in (b) above documents that identify the results of the design verifications.
O   (d) Identify, index, and file quality records for easy retrieval.
O   (e) Retain quality records for the time specified in the contract (if not specified they shall be retained for 10 years).
O   (f) Provide for the safe storing of records to minimize deterioration or damage and to prevent loss (the use of a double filing system is an acceptable method).
O   (g) Draw up a procedure for 3.2.4.

4. VERIFICATION OF QUALITY

4.1. INITIAL EVALUATION OF QUALITY ASSURANCE PROGRAMME, AND PHYSICAL RESOURCES

O   Prior to the award of a contract and performance of the activity, the customer shall evaluate the contractor's quality assurance programme and resources to determine whether the requirements of this chapter can be met.

In the event of the contractor not fulfilling all applicable requirements, the customer may award the contract provided that he takes the responsibility for those QA requirements that cannot be complied with by the contractor. In such a case, the exception shall be clearly defined in the contract.

4.2. CONTINUING EVALUATION AND VERIFICATION

M   The schedule and/or frequency of customer's and authorities' surveillance should be outlined in the contract.

If not otherwise specified in the contract, a maximum of two surveillances will be performed each year.

4.3. ACCESS

M   The contractor shall provide for reasonable access of the competent authorities and of the customer to his premises and records for surveillance purposes.

5. ATTACHMENT: SUMMARY OF THE REQUIREMENTS
The following summary of the requirements is given as a check-list to determine the applicable requirements to be included in a contract. An optional requirement ( ) becomes mandatory when the space between the brackets is filled in with a cross (X).

Clause	Title of Clauses, Content	(X) = applicable ( ) = not applicable
3.1.	Basic Requirements	
3.1.1.	Quality Assurance Programme	(X)
3.1.2.	Organization	
(a)	Representative for quality requirements	(X)
(b)	Management policies, responsibility and authority of personnel	( )
3.1.3.	Quality Assurance Documents	
3.1.3.1.	Quality Assurance Manual	
(a and b)	Preparation, submission, revision and content	( )
3.1.3.2.	Quality Assurance Procedures (General)	(X)
3.2.	Specific Requirements	
3.2.1.	Design Management	
3.2.1.1.	Design Input Requirements	
(a)	Identification and transmission	(X)
(b)	Review and agreement	(X)

Clause	Title of Clauses, Content	(X) = applicable ( ) = not applicable
3.2.1.2.	Design Process	
(a)	Procedure for establishment of design documents	(X)
(b)	Documentation for design analysis	(X)
(c)	Construction methods and data	(X)
3.2.1.3.	Interface Control	
(a)	Identification of organizational interfaces	(X)
(b)	Identification and documentation of interfacing design information	( )
(c)	Procedure	( )
3.2.1.4.	Design Verification	
(a)	Verification	(X)
(b)	Extent of verification	( )
(c)	Documentation	( )
(d)	Procedure	( )
3.2.1.5.	Design Changes	
(a)	Documentation	(X)
(b)	Identification and retrieval	( )
(c)	Procedure	( )
3.2.1.6.	Computer Programs	
(a)	Qualification, methods and documentation	(X)
3.2.2.	Document Control	
(a)	Approval	(X)
(b)	List of documents	( )
3.2.3.	Procurement of Design Activities	
3.2.3.1.	Selection of Subcontractors	
(a)	Applicable standards and requirements	(X)
(b)	Evaluation of subcontractors	( )

Clause	Title of Clauses, Content	(X) = applicable ( ) = not applicable
3.2.3.2.	Subcontract Requirements	
(a–c)	Activities and applicable standards	(X)
(d–f)	Submission of documents, right of access, review by quality assurance representative	( )
(g)	Approval	(X)
3.2.3.3.	Amendments to Subcontract	(X)
3.2.3.4.	Verification of the Quality Management System Implemented by a Subcontractor (as specified in the subcontract)	
3.2.4.	Quality Records	
(a)	Maintenance of quality records for design	(X)
(b)	Maintenance of quality records for the quality assurance programme and procurement	( )
(c)	Records of design verification	( )
(d–f)	Filing and storage	( )
(g)	Procedure	( )
4.	Verification of Quality	
4.1.	Initial Evaluation of the Quality Assurance Programme and Physical Resources	( )
4.2.	Continuing Evaluation and Verification	(X)
4.3.	Access	(X)

Quality Management Requirements D3

Contents

1. SCOPE   48

1.1. General   48
1.2. Applicability   48
1.3. Contractor's Responsibilities   48

2. DEFINITIONS   48

3. REQUIREMENTS   48

3.1. Basic Requirements   48
3.2. Specific Requirements   48
3.2.1. Design Management   48
3.2.1.1. Design Input Requirements   48
3.2.1.2. Design Process   49
3.2.1.3. Design Verification   49
3.2.1.4. Design Changes   49
3.2.1.5. Computer Programs   49
3.2.2. Document Control   49
3.2.3. Procurement of Design Activities   49
3.2.4. Quality Records   50

4. VERIFICATION OF QUALITY   50

4.1. Access   50

1. SCOPE

1.1. GENERAL

This chapter specifies requirements to be complied with by the contractor to ensure an efficient quality management in design.

1.2. APPLICABILITY

The requirements of this chapter apply to design activities when specified in a contract.

1.3. CONTRACTOR'S RESPONSIBILITIES

The contractor's responsibilities are:

(a) To comply with the customer's requirements as specified in the contract.
(b) To produce objective evidence that the design meets contractual requirements.
(c) To initiate corrective measures promptly when the quality assurance representative notifies the contractor of deviations from established requirements.

2. DEFINITIONS

Refer to Quality Management Directive.

3. REQUIREMENTS

3.1. BASIC REQUIREMENTS

Not applicable.

3.2. SPECIFIC REQUIREMENTS

3.2.1. Design Management

3.2.1.1. Design Input Requirements
Prior to the preparation of design documents, design

input shall be identified and transmitted in written form.
    Design input shall be reviewed and agreed by interfacing organizations.

3.2.1.2.   Design Process
Design documents shall specify important construction methods and data, such as:

— special treatments
— sequence of operations
— applicable specifications
— special equipment
— work methods.

3.2.1.3.   Design Verification
Specifications, design (conception) drawings and concepts of detailed drawings shall be subject to a verification performed by a competent person.
    Design calculations shall also be verified but the verification may be performed by the same person who did the initial calculations provided that a different calculation method is used.

3.2.1.4.   Design Changes
Design changes that affect construction documents shall be in writing.

3.2.1.5.   Computer Programs
Sophisticated computer programs shall be qualified and the qualification documented.

3.2.2.   Document Control

The contractor shall establish measures to ensure that design documents required by 3.2.1. are approved for release.

3.2.3.   Procurement of Design Activities

The contractor shall prepare a subcontract document that provides a clear description of the design activities to be procured including technical requirements by reference to codes, standards, design criteria, etc.

The contractor shall process amendments to subcontracts in the same way as the initial subcontract and reference the initial subcontract number in amendments.

3.2.4. *Quality Records*

The contractor shall maintain quality records as evidence that design meets the contractual requirements (drawings, specifications, calculations).

4. VERIFICATION OF QUALITY

4.1. ACCESS

If specified in the contract, the contractor shall provide for reasonable access of the customer to his premises and records for surveillance purposes.

Quality Management Requirements M1

Contents

1.	SCOPE	53
1.1.	General	53
1.2.	Applicability	53
1.3.	Contractor's Responsibilities	53
2.	DEFINITIONS	54
3.	REQUIREMENTS	54
3.1.	Basic Requirements	54
3.1.1.	Quality Assurance Programme	54
3.1.2.	Organization	54
3.1.3.	Quality Assurance Documents	56
3.1.3.1.	Quality Assurance Manual	56
3.1.3.2.	Quality Plan	57
3.1.3.3.	Quality Assurance Procedures	58
3.2.	Specific Requirements	58
3.2.1.	Design Management	58
3.2.2.	Document Control	59
3.2.3.	Procurement	60
3.2.3.1.	Selection of Subcontractors	60
3.2.3.2.	Subcontract Requirements	60
3.2.3.3.	Amendments to Subcontracts	61
3.2.3.4.	Verification of the Quality Management System Implemented by a Subcontractor	61
3.2.3.5.	Receiving Inspection	61
3.2.4.	Measuring and Testing Equipment	61
3.2.5.	Inspection and Test	62
3.2.6.	In-process Inspection	63
3.2.7.	Final Inspection	63
3.2.8.	Inspection Status	63
3.2.9.	Identification and Traceability	64
3.2.10.	Preservation, Handling and Storage	64

3.2.11. Manufacturing   64
3.2.12. Special Processes   65
3.2.13. Packaging and Shipping   65
3.2.14. Quality Records   65
3.2.15. Non-conformances   67
3.2.16. Customer-supplied Items   68
3.2.17. Corrective Action   68
3.2.18. Audits   68

4.   VERIFICATION OF QUALITY   70

4.1.   Initial Evaluation   70
4.1.1.   Quality Assurance Programme, Facilities and
         Physical Resources   70
4.1.2.   Quality Plan   70
4.2.   Continuing Evaluation and Verification   70
4.3.   Access   70

1. SCOPE

1.1. GENERAL

This chapter specifies requirements to be incorporated in a contractor's quality assurance programme for manufacturing. The contractor is responsible for planning and developing a programme that assures that all his management, design and technical responsibilities for quality are incorporated and executed effectively. The programme is aimed primarily at ensuring an efficient quality management in manufacturing and taking corrective actions, when necessary.

Planning and detailed written procedures are essential for specifying how such activities as the following, which affect quality, are to be performed and controlled:

(a) Design management.
(b) Procurement.
(c) Manufacturing.
(d) Special processes.
(e) Measuring and testing equipment.
(f) Inspection and test.
(g) Handling, storing, preservation, packaging and shipping.
(h) Item identification and traceability.
(i) Documentation and quality records.
(j) Disposition of non-conformances and corrective action.
(k) Quality audits and management reviews.

1.2. APPLICABILITY

The requirements of this chapter apply to the manufacturing of items, when specified in a contract.

1.3. CONTRACTOR'S RESPONSIBILITIES

The contractor's responsibilities are:

(a) To develop and implement the controls and quality assurance procedures, specified herein, that will promptly detect and dispose of, or prevent, non-conformances to contractual requirements.

(b) To comply with the customer's requirements as specified in the contract.

(c) To prepare a quality assurance manual which shall be submitted for the customer's concurrence before the contract is awarded or at the latest before the work starts, as required in 3.1.3.1.

(d) To prepare a quality plan which shall be submitted to the customer before the work starts, as required in 3.1.3.2.

(e) To update and resubmit the quality assurance manual and quality plan to reflect current practices when significant changes occur in the contractor's programme or organization in order to improve its effectiveness or to prevent recurrence of non-conformances.

(f) To initiate corrective measures promptly when the quality assurance representative notifies the contractor of deviations from established requirements.

2. DEFINITIONS

Refer to Quality Management Directive.

3. REQUIREMENTS

3.1. BASIC REQUIREMENTS

3.1.1. *Quality Assurance Programme*

The contractor shall plan, establish, implement and maintain a quality assurance programme that complies with the requirements of this chapter.

3.1.2. *Organization*

The contractor shall:

(a) Clearly define management policies, objectives and responsibilities for quality assurance, including the responsibility of each division within a multi-divisional organization. The responsibility and authority for quality of those managing and performing the work and of those auditing and verifying conformance to quality requirements shall be defined and their relationships shown on organization charts.

(b)   Provide for the review by management of the status and adequacy of the quality assurance programme.

(c)   Appoint a representative who shall report regularly to management at a level that ensures that quality assurance requirements are not subordinated to design, manufacturing, construction or delivery and define his authority to resolve quality matters. The customer shall be notified of the appointment in writing.

(d)   Define the responsibility and authority of personnel who are primarily responsible for quality assurance and their organizational independence during audits and define the responsibility and authority of personnel who are primarily responsible for quality control and their organizational independence to:

    (i)   identify and record quality problems
    (ii)   initiate or recommend or provide solutions through designated channels
    (iii)   verify the implementation of dispositions
    (iv)   control further processing, delivery or installation of a non-conforming item or service until the deficiency or unsatisfactory condition has been resolved.

Note that, generally, audit personnel shall not be within the pattern of daily activities.

(e)   Use competent persons for inspection, other than those performing or directly supervising the work being inspected, unless specifically designated otherwise in the quality plan. Such persons shall report to an adequate level of management, excluding direct reports to supervisors responsible for producing the work being inspected.

Generally, inspectors shall verify the conformance to the specifications and drawings. In cases of problems or difficulties, they shall request clarifications from the design or other competent organizations and initiate appropriate measures.

If examinations, being a part of the whole inspections, are performed and documented by works personnel, the extent of the inspections by the independent personnel may be reduced, if such has been provided for by the quality plan.

3.1.3. *Quality Assurance Documents*

3.1.3.1. *Quality Assurance Manual*
(a) The contractor shall:

  (i) Prepare a quality assurance manual, approved and signed by a senior management official, and submit it for the customer's concurrence before the contract is awarded or at the latest before the work starts. A quality assurance manual submitted under a previous contract or tender may be referred to.

  (ii) Review and update the manual to reflect current quality assurance policies and procedures and resubmit the resulting manual.

  (iii) Implement the programme according to the provisions specified in the manual.

(b) The quality assurance manual shall deal as appropriate with the following:

  (i) Organization — The manual shall define the organizational measures as specified in 3.1.2.

  (ii) Quality plan — The manual shall identify the group responsible for the quality plan specified in 3.1.3.2. and define its main principles and features in adequate procedures.

  (iii) Quality assurance procedures — Documented quality assurance procedures as specified in 3.1.3.3. shall be included or shall be outlined and cross-referenced. Referenced QA procedures shall be made available to the quality assurance representative.

  (iv) Manual review — A statement shall be incorporated for reviewing and updating the manual as specified in 3.1.3.1.(a)(ii).

3.1.3.2. *Quality Plan*
(a)   The contractor shall:

   (i)   Plan the inspection and test activities.
   (ii) Identify in the quality plan the inspections and tests to be performed on the items listed in the contract, in compliance with contractual and/or technical requirements.
   (iii) Submit the plan for the customer's concurrence following the award of the contract and before the work starts. Referenced inspection and test specifications and/or procedures shall be made available to the quality assurance representative during the implementation of the quality plan.
   (iv) Update the plan during the life of the contract to reflect current conditions of manufacturing, inspecting and testing and resubmit the plan to the customer.

(b)   The quality plan may be of any format to suit the contractor's system. The quality plan shall deal as appropriate with:

   (i)   Identification of the characteristics or items to be inspected and tested.
   (ii) Identification of required inspection, test and special process operations and their relative location in the manufacturing cycle. The contractor may include additional in-process inspection points for his own evaluation of quality which will not be subject to acceptance and witness by the quality assurance representative.
   (iii) Reference to inspection, test and special process procedures, standards, acceptance criteria and sampling plan, if any.
   (iv) Indication of hold points beyond which the activity shall not proceed until the required inspections or tests have shown satisfactory results and have been documented.
   (v)   Provisions for the customer to insert witness points at which activities are to be observed. The activity may nevertheless proceed

> beyond a witness point should the customer fail to attend in spite of due notification.

(c)   The quality plans for subcontracted items, when concurred with by the contractor, shall be submitted to the customer, as applicable, for concurrence and insertion of witness points.

3.1.3.3.   Quality Assurance Procedures
The contractor shall have procedures for the following specific requirements should they apply to the contract:

Design management	Clause 3.2.1.
Document control	Clause 3.2.2.
Procurement	Clause 3.2.3.
Measuring and testing equipment	Clause 3.2.4.
Inspection and test	Clause 3.2.5.
In-process inspection	Clause 3.2.6.
Final inspection	Clause 3.2.7.
Inspection status	Clause 3.2.8.
Identification and traceability	Clause 3.2.9.
Preservation, handling and storage	Clause 3.2.10.
Manufacturing	Clause 3.2.11.
Special processes	Clause 3.2.12.
Packaging and shipping	Clause 3.2.13.
Quality records	Clause 3.2.14.
Non-conformances	Clause 3.2.15.
Customer-supplied items	Clause 3.2.16.
Corrective action	Clause 3.2.17.
Audits	Clause 3.2.18.

Each QA procedure shall define, as applicable, such things as: its purpose and scope; who is responsible for what; how all steps are to be performed; what materials, equipment and documentation are to be used; how it is all controlled.

Forms used shall be exhibited.

QA procedures shall be updated when necessary.

3.2.   SPECIFIC REQUIREMENTS

3.2.1.   Design Management

Refer to chapter D1, D2 or D3 as applicable.

3.2.2.   *Document Control*

The contractor shall:

(a)   Establish measures to ensure that all essential quality related documents including but not limited to those listed below are reviewed for adequacy and approved for release by authorized personnel:

    (i)   Quality assurance manual required by 3.1.3.1.
    (ii)   Quality plan required by 3.1.3.2.
    (iii)   Quality assurance procedures required by 3.1.3.3.
    (iv)   Design documents required as a consequence of 3.2.1.
    (v)   Procurement documents required by 3.2.3.
    (vi)   Calibration procedures required by 3.2.4.
    (vii)   Inspection and test procedures required by 3.2.5.
    (viii)   Manufacturing documents required by 3.2.11.
    (ix)   Special process procedures required by 3.2.12.

(b)   Establish distribution lists for the above-mentioned documents, update and maintain them in the current form to assure that the proper personnel are issued with all the documents necessary to perform the work.

(c)   Make the applicable issues of these documents available at areas where these activities are performed.

(d)   Establish and update lists of applicable documents for manufacturing and distribute them systematically. Controlled distribution is required for these lists only.

(e)   Ensure that changes to documents receive the authorizations by the same organizations as the initial documents unless other organizations are specifically designated. Maintain a record of changes as they are made. Written notes or documents are acceptable provided that they are made by authorized persons according to established procedures. Documents shall be revised and re-issued after a practical number of changes have been issued.

3.2.3. Procurement

3.2.3.1. Selection of Subcontractors

The contractor shall identify items to be procured.
He shall undertake the following:

(a) Determine for these subcontracted items the applicable Quality Management Requirements. Classification to these Quality Management Requirements shall be in such a way that the overall quality is not impaired. The classification list shall be submitted to the customer for acceptance.

(b) Evaluate and select subcontractors in accordance with 4.1. of the applicable Quality Management Requirements with regard to their ability to meet subcontract and quality requirements.

(c) When 'off the shelf' items are to be procured, evaluation of subcontractor may not necessarily be required. The contractor shall nominate to the quality assurance representative those materials, parts and components that belong to this category.

3.2.3.2. Subcontract Requirements

The contractor shall include in subcontracts the following, as applicable:

(a) A clear description of the items or services to be procured including technical data and inspection and test requirements by reference to standards, technical specifications, drawings, etc.

(b) A designation of the applicable Quality Management Requirements to be applied to the items and exceptions, if any.

(c) A designation of the contractor's QA procedures to be implemented by the subcontractor, if applicable.

(d) Instructions for the submission, retention and disposition of quality records.

(e) Requirements for packaging and shipping.

(f) A statement related to the right of access to the subcontractor's premises and records for audit and/or surveillance by the contractor or the customer.

(g) Instructions for notification of witness points.

(h) Requirements for the subcontractor to report non-conformances.

(i) Applicable requirements to be extended to lower tier

subcontractors, if any.

Subcontract documents shall be reviewed and approved in accordance with 3.2.2.(a).

All unpriced subcontracts and associated reference data shall be made available on request for review by the quality assurance representative.

3.2.3.3. Amendments to Subcontracts

The contractor shall process amendments to subcontracts in the same way as the initial subcontract and reference the initial subcontract number in the amendments.

3.2.3.4. Verification of the Quality Management System Implemented by a Subcontractor

Refer to 4.2. of the applicable Quality Management Requirements.

3.2.3.5. Receiving Inspection

To the extent that is practical, receiving inspection shall be specified in the quality plan.

The contractor shall:

(a) Identify and inspect items on receipt to ascertain that they comply with contractual requirements. In determining the amount or nature of receiving inspection, consideration shall be given to the surveillance exercised at source and documented evidence of quality conformance. Receiving inspection shall cover as a minimum: verification of deterioration or damage during transport, identification control, review of required documentation.

(b) Initiate corrective action with subcontractors when non-conforming items are received, as required by the nature and frequency of non-conformances.

(c) Hold incoming items until the required inspection and/or test have been completed or the necessary inspection and/or test reports have been received and verified except when items are released under positive recall.

3.2.4. Measuring and Testing Equipment

All measuring and testing equipment and devices used to verify characteristics that can affect item quality shall be controlled and maintained. At prescribed intervals, or prior to use, they shall be calibrated and adjusted against certified equipment having a known valid relationship to nationally recognized standards. Where no national standards exist, the basis employed for calibration shall be documented.

No special calibration and control measures are necessary on rulers, tape measures, levels and other such devices, if normal commercial practices provide for adequate accuracy and/or if large tolerances are allowed for the corresponding measurements.

The contractor shall:

(a) Include in calibration procedures: equipment type, frequency of checks, description of check method, acceptance criteria and action to be taken when results are unsatisfactory. Exception will be allowed for measuring and testing equipment for which calibration is simple and does not require a specific detailed procedure. The contractor shall identify those types of measuring equipment for which he has not provided calibration procedures.

(b) Identify measuring and testing equipment with a tag, sticker, or other suitable indicator to show the calibration status.

(c) Maintain calibration records for measuring and testing equipment.

(d) Assess and document the validity of previous inspection and test results when measuring and testing equipment are found to be out of calibration.

3.2.5. Inspection and Test

(a) The contractor shall provide for the performance of inspections and tests as specified in the quality plan. These inspections and tests shall be carried out in accordance with written procedures which define the method, the materials, instruments or equipment to be used and acceptance/rejection criteria.

The contractor shall amend the selected inspection methods in cases where their unsuitability is demonstrated.

(b) Inspections and tests shall be documented on inspection and test reports which identify as a minimum the item inspected or tested, applicable drawings, specifications or procedures, the date of inspection or test, the inspector, tester or data recorder, the type of observation, the results, the acceptability and the action taken in connection with any deficiencies identified.

3.2.6. In-process Inspection

The contractor shall:

(a) Identify, inspect and/or test items as required by the quality plan.
(b) Monitor process methods, where inspection is not feasible.
(c) Hold items until the required inspections and/or tests have been completed or the necessary reports have been received and verified except when items are released under positive recall. Release under positive recall shall not preclude (a) above.

3.2.7. Final Inspection

The contractor shall:

(a) Identify, inspect and/or test the completed item as required by the quality plan.
(b) Verify that the item has been inspected at all points shown in the quality plan and that the records are adequate and complete.

3.2.8. Inspection Status

The contractor shall:

(a) Provide means for assuring that required inspections and tests are performed and that the acceptability of items with regard to inspections and tests performed is known throughout manufacturing.
(b) Establish and maintain a system for identifying the inspection/acceptance status by means of tags, stamped impressions, or other physical means to be affixed to the item or its container or by means of inspection records.
(c) Show the identity of the contractor and his inspector

on any inspection marking used.

(d) Provide for measures for controlling status indicators including the authority for application and removal of tags, stamps or other marking.

(e) Identify non-conforming items.

3.2.9. *Identification and Traceability*

The contractor shall establish and maintain an adequate system to:

(a) Identify each item (lot, component or part) to the applicable drawing, specification or other technical document, throughout the whole manufacturing process and up to the actual delivery.

(b) Assign to each item a unique identification where specific traceability is required by the contract.

(c) Record this identification on all process, inspection and test records, where traceability is specified.

3.2.10. *Preservation, Handling and Storage*

The contractor shall:

(a) Establish, maintain and document a system for the preservation, storage and handling of all items from the time of receipt through the entire manufacturing process and subsequent storage to prevent abuse, misuse, damage, deterioration or loss.

(b) Periodically inspect stored items for condition and shelf-life expiry.

(c) Inspect and test special handling tools and equipment at specific times to verify that the tools and equipment are adequately maintained and will not damage the items and will ensure safe and adequate handling.

3.2.11. *Manufacturing*

The contractor shall:

(a) Ensure that all manufacturing activities are carried out under controlled conditions. These include documented work instructions such as route cards, shop travellers, production programmes, etc., defining the sequences of manufacturing or processing and including criteria for workmanship, suitable manufacturing equipment and any special working environment necessary.

(b)   Control prior to release for manufacturing all jigs, fixtures, tooling masters, templates and patterns used for verifying quality. The extent and frequency of tool control shall be defined.

3.2.12. *Special Processes*

The contractor shall:

(a)   Identify those special processes subject to the requirements of this clause. Special processes shall include welding, heat treating and non-destructive examination, as applicable.

(b)   Establish documented procedures to assure that these processes are accomplished under controlled conditions by qualified personnel using qualified documented procedures and suitable equipment in accordance with applicable codes, standards, specifications, criteria and contractual requirements.

(c)   Maintain documentation for currently qualified personnel and processes according to the requirements of pertinent codes and standards.

(d)   Define the necessary qualifications of personnel and procedures for special processes not covered by existing codes or standards, or where item or service quality requirements exceed the requirements of established codes or standards.

(e)   Include special processes in the quality plan.

3.2.13. *Packaging and Shipping*

The contractor shall inspect the cleaning, preservation, packaging and marking and verify shipping operations to ensure that contractual requirements are met.

3.2.14. *Quality Records*

The contractor shall:

(a)   Maintain quality records as evidence that:

(i)   The quality assurance programme meets the requirements of these Quality Management

Requirements (manual, procedures, quality plan).

(ii) The items or services meet contractual or other applicable technical requirements (specifications, drawings, calculations, manufacturing, inspection and test procedures).

(iii) Personnel and procedures for special processes are qualified as required by 3.2.12.(c).

(iv) Measuring and testing equipment is calibrated as required by 3.2.4.

(v) The procurements meet the requirements of 3.2.3.

(vi) Corrective actions are being taken and are effective as required by 3.2.17.

(vii) Audits are performed as required by 3.2.18.

(b) Maintain final performance quality records which include as appropriate:

(i) Contractor's certificate of compliance.

(ii) As-built records.

(iii) Material test reports or certificates.

(iv) Non-destructive examination records or certificates (including radiographs).

(v) Inspection and test records.

(vi) Heat treatment records or records that document the characteristics achieved after heat treating, as applicable.

(vii) Non-conformance reports.

Items (iv), (v) and (vi) apply to those operations performed after receipt of material from the supplier.

(c) Identify, index and file quality records for easy retrieval.

(d) Retain quality records for the time specified in the contract. If not specified, final performance quality records shall be retained for 10 years.

(e) Provide a suitable environment for storing of records in order to minimize deterioration or damage and to prevent loss (the use of a double filing system is an acceptable method).

(f) Submit the certificate of compliance along with the shipment.

3.2.15. *Non-conformances*

The contractor is responsible for the identification and disposition of all non-conforming items, including those of subcontractors. Final acceptance of the contractor's disposition of those items that violate contractual requirements is the prerogative of the customer.

The contractor shall:

(a)   Establish and maintain measures for controlling non-conforming items that:

    (i)   Define the responsibility and authority of those who dispose of non-conforming items. This shall include provision for a technical review that involves those who are responsible for design, manufacturing, and quality functions, if these functions are concerned.

    (ii)   Detect and record non-conformances promptly, unless these are corrected immediately in accordance with common manufacturing practices.

    (iii)   Identify and hold non-conforming items for evaluation; these need not be held if subsequent work is not affected.

    (iv)   Develop a disposition that has the concurrence of all responsible parties.

    (v)   Implement accepted dispositions. This shall include requirements for re-inspecting and retesting repaired and reworked items.

    (vi)   Verify the implementation of accepted dispositions.

(b)   Provide holding areas or methods for segregating non-conforming items to prevent unauthorized use, shipment, or mixing with conforming items. However, where physical segregation is not practical or the non-conformance is not clearly visible, tagging, marking or other positive means of identification is acceptable.

(c)   Maintain records that identify non-conforming items, the nature and extent of non-conformance, its disposition and objective evidence that repaired and reworked items have been re-inspected or retested according to applicable procedures.

3.2.16. Customer-supplied Items

The customer is responsible for specifying in the contract the Quality Management Requirements applicable for items supplied by himself to the contractor and for certifying that these items are consistent with the quality requirements of the final item.

The contractor shall:

(a) Verify customer certification.
(b) Examine customer-supplied items on receipt for completeness and proper type and to detect transit damage. Further receiving inspection is not required unless the contractor needs actual characteristics for subsequent work or unless specified in the contract. Examination may be deferred until further processing is scheduled if items are in sealed containers or have special preservation or packaging.
(c) Control customer-supplied items from receipt onwards according to the requirements of this standard.
(d) Report promptly in writing to the quality assurance representative any customer-supplied items found damaged, lost, non-conforming, or otherwise unsuitable or unnecessary for use either on receipt or while in the contractor's custody.

3.2.17. Corrective Action

The contractor shall:

(a) Investigate the causes of significant or recurring non-conformances and take appropriate action to prevent repetition.
(b) Document and have reported to appropriate levels of the contractor's management causes of significant conditions that adversely affect quality and the corrective action taken.

3.2.18. Audits

(a) The contractor shall establish, implement and document a plan for audit which objectively evaluates and verifies that:

(i)   He is complying with all aspects of his quality assurance programme, documented quality programme procedures and specified requirements.

(ii)   The quality assurance programme is performing adequately.

(iii) Recommended corrective actions are being implemented effectively.

(iv) Deficient areas are being re-audited.

(b)   The audit plan shall define:

(i)   Functional areas to be audited.

(ii)   Assignments of those performing the audits.

(iii) Frequency of audits.

(iv) Methods for reporting findings and recommendations.

(v)   The means for having corrective actions initiated and implemented.

(c)   Audits shall include an evaluation of:

(i)   Work areas, activities, processes, items and services being produced.

(ii)   Quality assurance practices, documented procedures, and instructions.

(iii) Documents and records.

(d)   Appropriately trained personnel who are not directly responsible for the area being audited shall perform the audits according to documented audit procedures or check-lists that identify the essential characteristics to be verified; all auditors shall have professional experience in the field they audit.

(e)   Management responsible for the area audited shall review and correct deficiencies identified in the documented audit results.

4. VERIFICATION OF QUALITY

4.1. INITIAL EVALUATION

4.1.1. *Quality Assurance Programme, Facilities and Physical Resources*

Prior to the award of a contract, and to the performance of the activity, the customer shall evaluate the contractor's quality assurance programme, manufacturing facilities and resources to determine whether the requirements of this section can be met.

In the event of the contractor not fulfilling all applicable requirements, the customer may award the contract provided that he takes the responsibility for those QA requirements that will not be met by the contractor. In such a case, the exceptions shall be clearly defined in the contract.

4.1.2. *Quality Plan*

The customer shall evaluate the quality plan and all revisions thereto in order to determine its acceptability.

The customer shall indicate his witness points on the accepted quality plan.

4.2. CONTINUING EVALUATION AND VERIFICATION

The schedule or frequency of the customer's and authorities' audits should be outlined in the contract.

If not otherwise specified in the contract, a maximum of one audit will be performed each year.

In addition, the customer shall perform surveillances according to the accepted quality plan.

4.3. ACCESS

The contractor shall provide for reasonable access of the competent authorities and of the customer to his premises and records for audit and surveillance purposes.

Quality Management Requirements M2A

Contents

1.	SCOPE	73
1.1.	General	73
1.2.	Applicability	73
1.3.	Contractor's Responsibilities	73
2.	DEFINITIONS	74
3.	REQUIREMENTS	74
3.1.	Basic Requirements	74
3.1.1.	Quality Assurance Programme	74
3.1.2.	Organization	74
3.1.3.	Quality Assurance Documents	75
3.1.3.1.	Quality Assurance Manual	75
3.1.3.2.	Quality Plan	76
3.1.3.3.	Quality Assurance Procedures	77
3.2.	Specific Requirements	78
3.2.1.	Design Management	78
3.2.2.	Document Control	78
3.2.3.	Procurement	79
3.2.3.1.	Selection of Subcontractors	79
3.2.3.2.	Subcontract Requirements	80
3.2.3.3.	Amendments to Subcontracts	80
3.2.3.4.	Verification of the Quality Management System Implemented by a Subcontractor	80
3.2.3.5.	Receiving Inspection	80
3.2.4.	Measuring and Testing Equipment	81
3.2.5.	Inspection and Test	82
3.2.6.	In-process Inspection	82
3.2.7.	Final Inspection	82
3.2.8.	Inspection Status	83
3.2.9.	Identification and Traceability	83
3.2.10.	Preservation, Handling and Storage	83

3.2.11. Manufacturing   84
3.2.12. Special Processes   84
3.2.13. Packaging and Shipping   84
3.2.14. Quality Records   85
3.2.15. Non-conformances   86
3.2.16. Customer-supplied Items   87

4.   VERIFICATION OF QUALITY   87

4.1.   Initial Evaluation   87
4.1.1. Quality Assurance Programme, Facilities and
       Physical Resources   87
4.1.2. Quality Plan   88
4.2.   Continuing Evaluation and Verification   88
4.3.   Access   88

1. SCOPE

1.1. GENERAL

This chapter specifies requirements to be incorporated in a contractor's quality assurance programme for manufacturing. It covers the first part of QA level 2. The contractor is responsible for planning and developing a programme that assures that all his management and technical responsibilities for quality are incorporated and executed effectively. The programme is aimed primarily at ensuring an efficient quality management in manufacturing.

Planning and detailed written procedures are essential for specifying how such activities as the following, which affect quality, are to be performed and controlled:

(a) Design management.
(b) Procurement.
(c) Manufacturing.
(d) Special processes.
(e) Measuring and testing equipment.
(f) Inspection and testing.
(g) Handling, storing, preservation, packaging and shipping.
(h) Item identification and traceability.
(i) Documentation and quality records.
(j) Disposition of non-conformances.

1.2. APPLICABILITY

The requirements of this chapter apply to the manufacturing of items, when specified in a contract.

1.3. CONTRACTOR'S RESPONSIBILITIES

The contractor's responsibilities are:

(a) To develop and implement the controls and quality assurance procedures specified herein that will promptly detect and dispose of non-conformances to contractual requirements.

(b)   To comply with the customer's requirements as specified in the contract.

(c)   To prepare a quality assurance manual which shall be submitted to the customer at the latest before the work starts, as required in 3.1.3.1.

(d)   To prepare a quality plan which shall be submitted to the customer before the work starts, as required in 3.1.3.2.

(e)   To update and resubmit the quality assurance manual and quality plan to reflect current practices when significant changes occur in the contractor's programme or organization in order to improve its effectiveness.

(f)   To initiate corrective measures promptly when the quality assurance representative notifies the contractor of deviations from established requirements.

2. DEFINITIONS

Refer to Quality Management Directive.

3. REQUIREMENTS

3.1. BASIC REQUIREMENTS

3.1.1. *Quality Assurance Programme*

The contractor shall plan, establish, implement and maintain a quality assurance programme that complies with the requirements of this chapter.

3.1.2. *Organization*

The contractor shall:

(a)   Clearly define management policies, objectives and responsiblities for quality assurance including the responsibility of each division within a multi-divisional organization. The responsibility and authority for quality of those managing and performing the work and of those verifying conformance to quality requirements shall be defined and their relationships shown on organization charts.

(b) Appoint a representative who shall report regularly to management at a level that ensures that quality assurance requirements are not subordinated to manufacturing or delivery and define his authority to resolve quality matters.

(c) Define the responsibility and authority of personnel who are primarily responsible for quality control and their organizational independence to:

    (i) identify and record quality problems

    (ii) initiate or recommend or provide solutions through designated channels

    (iii) verify the implementation of dispositions

    (iv) control further processing, delivery or installation of a non-conforming item until the deficiency or unsatisfactory condition has been resolved.

(d) Use competent persons for inspection other than those performing or directly supervising the work being inspected unless specifically designated otherwise in the quality plan. Such persons shall report to an adequate level of management, excluding direct reports to supervisors responsible for producing the work being inspected.

Generally inspectors shall verify the conformance to the specifications and drawings. In cases of problems or difficulties, they shall request clarifications from the design or other competent organizations and initiate appropriate measures.

If examinations, being a part of the whole inspections, are performed and documented by works personnel, the extent of the inspections by the independent personnel may be reduced, if such has been provided for by the quality plan.

3.1.3. *Quality Assurance Documents*

3.1.3.1. *Quality Assurance Manual*
(a) The contractor shall:

    (i) Prepare a quality assurance manual approved and signed by a senior

> management official and submit it for the customer's concurrence before the contract is awarded or at the latest before the work starts. A quality assurance manual submitted under a previous contract or tender may be referred to.
>
> (ii) Review and update the manual to reflect current quality assurance policies and resubmit the resulting manual.
>
> (iii) Implement the programme according to the provisions specified in the manual.

(b) The quality assurance manual shall deal with but need not be limited to the following:

> (i) Organization — The manual shall define the organizational measures as specified in 3.1.2.
>
> (ii) Quality plan — The manual shall identify the group responsible for the quality plan specified in 3.1.3.2. and define its main principles and features in adequate procedures.
>
> (iii) Quality assurance procedures — Quality assurance procedures specified in 3.1.3.3. shall be included or shall be outlined. QA procedures shall be made available to the quality assurance representative.
>
> (iv) Manual review — A statement shall be incorporated for reviewing and updating the manual as specified in 3.1.3.1(a)(ii).

3.1.3.2. *Quality Plan*

(a) The contractor shall:

> (i) Plan the inspection and test activities.
>
> (ii) Identify in the quality plan the inspections and tests to be performed on the items listed in the contract in compliance with contractual and/or technical requirements.
>
> (iii) Submit the plan for the customer's concurrence following the award of the contract and before the work starts. Referenced inspection and test specifications and/or procedures shall be made available to

the quality assurance representative during the implementation of the quality plan.

  (iv) Update the plan during the life of the contract to reflect current conditions of manufacturing, inspecting and testing and resubmit the plan to the customer.

(b) The quality plan may be of any format to suit the contractor's system. The quality plan shall deal as appropriate with:

  (i) Identification of the characteristics or items to be inspected and tested.

  (ii) Identification of required inspection, test and special process operations and their relative location in the manufacturing cycle. The contractor may include additional in-process inspection points for his own evaluation of quality which will not be subject to acceptance and witness by the quality assurance representative.

  (iii) Reference of inspection, test and special process procedures, standards, acceptance criteria and sampling plan, if any.

  (iv) Indication of hold points beyond which the activity shall not proceed until the required inspection or tests have shown satisfactory results and have been documented.

  (v) Provisions for the customer to insert witness points at which activities are to be observed.
    The activity may nevertheless proceed beyond a witness point should the customer fail to attend in spite of due notification.

(c) The quality plans for subcontracted items, when concurred with by the contractor, shall be submitted to the customer, as applicable, for concurrence and insertion of witness points.

3.1.3.3. *Quality Assurance Procedures*
The contractor shall have procedures for the following specific requirements if they apply to the contract:

Design management   Clause 3.2.1.
Document control   Clause 3.2.2.

Procurement	Clause 3.2.3.
Measuring and testing equipment	Clause 3.2.4.
Inspection and test	Clause 3.2.5.
In-process inspection	Clause 3.2.6.
Final inspection	Clause 3.2.7.
Inspection status	Clause 3.2.8.
Identification and traceability	Clause 3.2.9.
Special processes	Clause 3.2.12.
Packaging and shipping	Clause 3.2.13.
Quality records	Clause 3.2.14.
Non-conformances	Clause 3.2.15.
Customer-supplied items	Clause 3.2.16.

Each QA procedure shall define, as applicable, such things as: its purpose and scope; who is responsible for what; how all steps are to be performed; what materials, equipment and documentation are to be used; how it is all controlled.

Forms used shall be exhibited.

QA procedures shall be updated when necessary and made available to the quality assurance representative.

3.2. SPECIFIC REQUIREMENTS

3.2.1. *Design Management*

Refer to chapter D1, D2 or D3 as applicable.

3.2.2. *Document Control*

The contractor shall:

(a) Establish measures to ensure that all essential quality related documents including but not limited to those listed below are reviewed for adequacy and approved for release by authorized personnel:

    (i) Quality assurance manual required by 3.1.3.1.
    (ii) Quality plan required by 3.1.3.2.
    (iii) Quality assurance procedures required by 3.1.3.3.
    (iv) Design documents required as a consequence of 3.2.1.
    (v) Procurement documents required by 3.2.3.
    (vi) Calibration procedures required by 3.2.4.

(vii) Inspection and test procedures required by 3.2.5.

(viii) Special process procedures required by 3.2.12.

(b) Establish distribution lists for the above-mentioned documents as necessary, update and maintain them in the current form to assure that the proper personnel are issued with all the documents necessary to perform the work.

(c) Make the applicable issues of these documents available at areas where activities are performed.

(d) Establish and update lists of applicable documents for manufacturing and distribute them systematically. Controlled distribution is required for these lists only.

(e) Ensure that changes to documents receive the authorizations by the same organizations as the initial documents unless other organizations are specifically designated. Maintain a record of changes as they are made. Written notes on documents are acceptable provided that they are made by authorized persons according to established procedures. Documents shall be revised and re-issued after a practical number of changes have been issued.

3.2.3. *Procurement*

3.2.3.1. *Selection of Subcontractors*

The contractor shall identify items to be procured.

He shall undertake the following:

(a) Determine for these subcontracted items the applicable Quality Management Requirements. Classification to these Quality Management Requirements shall be in such a way that the overall quality is not impaired. The classification list shall be submitted to the customer for acceptance.

(b) Evaluate and select subcontractors in accordance with 4.1. of this chapter, if applicable, with regard to their ability to meet subcontract and quality requirements.

(c) When 'off the shelf' items are to be procured, evaluation of subcontractors may not necessarily be required. The contractor shall nominate to the quality assurance representative those items that belong to this category.

3.2.3.2.   Subcontract Requirements
The contractor shall include in subcontracts the following, as applicable:

(a)   A clear description of the items to be procured including technical data and inspection and test requirements by reference to technical specifications, drawings, etc.

(b)   A designation of the Quality Management Requirements and exceptions, if any.

(c)   A designation of the contractor's QA procedures to be implemented by the subcontractor, if applicable.

(d)   Requirements for packaging and shipping.

(e)   A statement related to the right of access to the subcontractor's premises and records for surveillance by the contractor or the customer.

(f)   Instruction for the submission, retention and disposition of quality records.

(g)   Instructions for notification of witness points.

(h)   Requirements for the subcontractor to report non-conformances.

Subcontract documents shall be reviewed and approved in accordance with 3.2.2.

All unpriced subcontracts and associated reference data shall be available on request for review by the quality assurance representative.

3.2.3.3.   Amendments to Subcontracts
The contractor shall process amendments to subcontracts in the same way as the initial subcontract and reference the initial subcontract number in the amendments.

3.2.3.4.   Verification of the Quality Management System Implemented by a Subcontractor
Refer to clause 4.2. of this chapter, if applicable.

3.2.3.5.   Receiving Inspection
To the extent that is practical, receiving inspection shall be specified in the quality plan.
The contractor shall:

(a)   Identify and inspect items on receipt to ascertain that they comply with contractual requirements. In determining the amount or nature of receiving inspection, consideration shall be given to the surveillance exercised at source and documented evidence of quality conformance. Receiving inspection shall cover as a minimum: verification of deterioration or damage during transport, identification control, review of required documentation.

(b) Initiate corrective action with subcontractors when non-conforming items are received, as required by the nature and frequency of non-conformances.

(c) Hold incoming items until the required inspection and/or test have been completed or the necessary inspection and/or test reports have been received and verified except when items are released under positive recall.

3.2.4. Measuring and Testing Equipment

All measuring and testing equipment and devices used to verify characteristics that can affect item quality shall be controlled and maintained. At prescribed intervals, or prior to use, they shall be calibrated and adjusted against certified equipment having a known valid relationship to nationally recognized standards. Where no national standards exist, the basis employed for calibration shall be documented.

No special calibration and control measures are necessary on rulers, tape measures, levels and other such devices, if normal commercial practices provide for adequate accuracy and/or if large tolerances are allowed for the corresponding measurements.

The contractor shall:

(a) Include in calibration procedures: equipment type, frequency of checks, description of check method, acceptance criteria and action to be taken when results are unsatisfactory. Exceptions will be allowed for measuring and testing equipment for which calibration is simple and does not require a specific detailed procedure. The contractor shall identify those types of measuring equipment for which he has not provided documented calibration procedures.

(b) Identify measuring and testing equipment with a tag, sticker, or other suitable indicator to show the calibration status.

(c) Maintain calibration records for measuring and testing equipment.

(d) Assess and document the validity of previous inspection and test results when measuring and test equipment are found to be out of calibration.

3.2.5. Inspection and Test

(a) The contractor shall provide for the performance of inspections and tests as specified in the quality plan. These inspections and tests shall be carried out in accordance with written procedures that define the method, the materials, instruments or equipment to be used and acceptance/rejection criteria.

The contractor shall amend the selected inspection methods in cases where their unsuitability is demonstrated.

(b) Inspections and tests shall be documented on inspection and test reports which shall identify as a minimum the item inspected or tested, applicable drawings, specifications or procedures, the date of inspection or test, the inspector, tester or data recorder, the type of observation, the results, the acceptability and the action taken in connection with any deficiencies identified.

3.2.6. In-process Inspection

The contractor shall:

(a) Identify, inspect and/or test items as required by the quality plan.

(b) Monitor process methods, where inspection is not feasible.

(c) Hold items until the required inspections and/or tests have been completed or necessary reports have been received and verified except when items are released under positive recall. Release under positive recall shall not preclude (a) above.

3.2.7. Final Inspection

The contractor shall:

(a) Identify, inspect and/or test the final item as required by the quality plan.
(b) Verify that the item has been inspected at all points shown in the quality plan and that the records are adequate and complete.

3.2.8. *Inspection Status*

The contractor shall provide means for assuring that required inspections and tests are performed and that the acceptability of items with regard to inspections and tests performed is known throughout manufacturing. The contractor shall identify non-conforming items.

3.2.9. *Identification and Traceability*

The contractor shall establish and maintain an adequate system to:

(a) Identify each item (lot, component or part) to the applicable drawing, specification or other technical document, throughout the whole manufacturing process and up to final delivery.
(b) Assign to each item a unique identification where specific traceability is required by the contract.
(c) Record this identification on all process, inspection and test records, where traceability is specified.

3.2.10. *Preservation, Handling and Storage*

This clause is to be used as a guideline only. No procedure is required.

The contractor should:

(a) Establish and maintain a system for the preservation, storage and handling of all items from the time of receipt through the entire manufacturing process and subsequent storage to prevent abuse, misuse, damage, deterioration or loss.
(b) Inspect stored items periodically for condition and shelf-life expiry.
(c) Inspect and test special handling tools and equipment at specific times to verify that the tools and equipment are adequately maintained and will not damage the items and will ensure safe and adequate handling.

3.2.11. Manufacturing

This clause is to be used as a guideline only. No procedure is required.

The contractor should:

(a) Ensure that all manufacturing activities are carried out under controlled conditions. These include documented work instructions such as route cards, shop travellers, production programmes, etc., that define the sequence of manufacturing or processing and include criteria for workmanship, suitable manufacturing equipment and any special working environment.

(b) Control prior to release for manufacturing all jigs, fixtures, tooling masters, templates and patterns used for verifying quality. The extent and frequency of tool control should be defined.

3.2.12. Special Processes

The contractor shall:

(a) Identify those special processes subject to the requirements of this clause. Special processes shall include welding, heat treating and non-destructive examination, as applicable.

(b) Establish documented procedures to assure that these processes are accomplished under controlled conditions by qualified personnel using qualified documented procedures and suitable equipment in accordance with applicable codes, standards, specifications, criteria and contractual requirements.

(c) Maintain documentation for currently qualified personnel and processes according to the requirements of pertinent codes and standards.

(d) Define the necessary qualifications of personnel and procedures for special processes not covered by existing codes or standards, or where items or service quality requirements exceed the requirements of established codes or standards.

(e) Include special processes in the quality plan.

3.2.13. Packaging and Shipping

The contractor shall inspect the cleaning, preservation,

packaging and marking and verify shipping operations to ensure that contractual requirements are met.

3.2.14. *Quality Records*

The contractor shall:

(a) Maintain quality records as evidence that:

   (i) The quality assurance programme meets the requirements of these Quality Management Requirements (manual, procedures, quality plan).

   (ii) The items or services meet contractual or other applicable technical requirements (specifications, drawings, calculations, manufacturing, inspection and test procedures).

   (iii) Personnel and procedures for special processes are qualified as required by 3.2.12.(c).

   (iv) Measuring and test equipment are calibrated as required by 3.2.4.

   (v) The procurements meet the requirements of 3.2.3.

(b) Maintain final performance quality records that include as appropriate:

   (i) Contractor's certificate of compliance.

   (ii) As-built records.

   (iii) Materials test reports or certificates.

   (iv) Non-destructive examination records or certificates.

   (v) Inspection and test records.

   (vi) Heat treatment records or records that document the characteristics achieved after heat treating, as applicable.

   (vii) Non-conformance reports.

   Items (iv), (v) and (vi) apply to those operations performed after receipt of material from the supplier.

(c) Identify, index and file quality records for easy retrieval.

(d)   Retain quality records for the time specified in the contract. If not specified, final performance quality records shall be retained for 10 years.

(e)   Provide for the safe storing of records in order to minimize deterioration or damage and to prevent loss (the use of a double filing system is an acceptable method).

(f)   Submit the certificates of compliance along with shipments.

3.2.15. *Non-conformances*

The contractor is responsible for the identification and disposition of all non-conforming items, including those of subcontractors. Final acceptance of the contractor's disposition of those items that violate contractual requirements is the prerogative of the customer.

The contractor shall:

(a)   Establish and maintain measures for controlling non-conforming items that:

(i)   Define the responsibility and authority of those who dispose of non-conforming items. This shall include provision for a technical review that involves those who are responsible for design, manufacturing, and quality functions, if these functions are concerned.

(ii)   Detect and record non-conformances promptly except if corrected immediately in accordance with common manufacturing practices.

(iii)   Identify and hold non-conforming items for evaluation; these need not be held if subsequent work is not affected.

(iv)   Develop a disposition that has the concurrence of all responsible parties.

(v)   Implement accepted dispositions. This shall include requirements for re-inspecting and retesting repaired and reworked items.

(vi)   Verify the implementation of accepted dispositions.

(b)   Provide holding areas or methods for segregating non-conforming items to prevent unauthorized use, shipment or mixing with conforming items. However, where physical segregation is not practical or the non-conformance is not clearly visible, tagging, marking or other positive means of identification is acceptable.

(c) Maintain records that identify non-conforming items, the nature and extent of non-conformance, its disposition, and objective evidence that repaired and reworked items have been re-inspected or retested according to applicable procedures.

3.2.16. *Customer-supplied Items*

The customer is responsible for specifying in the contract the Quality Management Requirements applicable for items supplied by himself to the contractor and for certifying that these items are consistent with the quality requirements of the final item.

The contractor shall:

(a) Verify customer certification.
(b) Examine customer-supplied items on receipt for completeness and proper type and to detect transit damage. Further receiving inspection is not required unless the contractor needs actual characteristics for subsequent work or unless specified in the contract. Examination may be deferred until further processing is scheduled if items are in sealed containers or have special preservation or packaging.
(c) Control customer-supplied items from receipt onwards according to the requirements of this standard.
(d) Report promptly in writing to the quality assurance representative any customer-supplied items found damaged, lost, non-conforming, or otherwise unsuitable or unnecessary for use either on receipt or while in the contractor's custody.

4. VERIFICATION OF QUALITY

4.1. INITIAL EVALUATION

4.1.1. *Quality Assurance Programme, Facilities and Physical Resources*

Prior to the award of a contract, and to the performance of

the activity, the customer shall evaluate the contractor's quality assurance programme, manufacturing facilities and resources to determine whether the requirements of this section can be met.

In the event of the contractor not fulfilling all applicable requirements, the customer may award the contract provided that he takes the responsibility for those QA requirements that will not be met by the contractor. In such a case, the exceptions shall be clearly defined in the contract.

4.1.2. Quality Plan

The customer shall evaluate the quality plan and all revisions thereto in order to determine its acceptability.

The customer shall indicate his witness point on the accepted quality plan.

4.2. CONTINUING EVALUATION AND VERIFICATION

The customer shall perform surveillances according to the quality plan.

4.3. ACCESS

The contractor shall provide for reasonable access of the competent authorities and of the customer to his premises and records for surveillance purposes.

Quality Management Requirements M2B

Contents

1. SCOPE   90

1.1. General   90
1.2. Applicability   90
1.3. Contractor's Responsibilities   90

2. DEFINITIONS   90

3. REQUIREMENTS   90

3.1. Basic Requirements   90
3.1.1. Inspection Programme   90
3.1.2. Organization   91
3.1.3. Quality Assurance Documents   91
3.2. Specific Requirements   91
3.2.1. Measuring and Testing Equipment   91
3.2.2. Inspection and Test   92
3.2.3. Quality Records   92
3.2.4. Non-conformances   92
3.2.5. Customer-supplied Items   93

4. VERIFICATION OF QUALITY   94

4.1. Access   94

1. SCOPE

1.1. GENERAL

This chapter specifies requirements to be incorporated in a contractor's inspection programme for manufacturing. It covers the second part of QA level 2. The contractor is responsible for planning a programme that detects and disposes of non-conforming items and provides objective evidence that contractual requirements are met.

1.2. APPLICABILITY

The requirements of this chapter apply to the manufacturing of items when specified in a contract.

1.3. CONTRACTOR'S RESPONSIBILITIES

The contractor's responsibilities are:

(a) To develop and implement the inspection activities specified herein that detect and dispose of non-conformance to contractual requirements.
(b) To comply with the customer's requirements as specified in the contract.
(c) To produce objective evidence that items meet contractual requirements.
(d) To initiate corrective measures promptly when the quality assurance representative notifies the contractor of deviations from established requirements.

2. DEFINITIONS

Refer to Quality Management Directive.

3. REQUIREMENTS

3.1. BASIC REQUIREMENTS

3.1.1. Inspection Programme

The contractor shall establish and maintain an inspection

programme that complies with the requirements of this chapter.

3.1.2. Organization

The contractor shall:

(a) Appoint a representative authorized to resolve quality matters.
(b) Use competent persons for inspection, other than those performing the work being inspected, unless specifically designated otherwise in the inspection programme.

3.1.3. Quality Assurance Documents

The quality assurance documents include the inspection programme required by 3.1.1. and procedure for handling of non-conformances in accordance with the requirements of 3.2.4.

The contractor shall:

(a) Submit the inspection programme for the customer's concurrence before the works start.
(b) Review and update the inspection programme to reflect current practices and resubmit the resulting programme.
(c) Update the non-conformance procedure when necessary and make it available to the quality assurance representative.

3.2. SPECIFIC REQUIREMENTS

3.2.1. Measuring and Testing Equipment

No special calibration and control measures are necessary on rulers, tape measures, levels and other such devices, if normal commercial practices provide for adequate accuracy and/or if large tolerances are allowed for the corresponding measurements.

In all other cases, the contractor shall provide objective evidence that measuring and testing equipment:

    (a)   is in a known state of calibration
    (b)   can provide for valid measurements.

3.2.2. Inspection and Test

The contractor shall:

(a) Plan the inspection and/or testing activities (inspection programme).
(b) Inspect and/or test the items as planned and in accordance with written procedures that define the method, the equipment to be used and acceptance/rejection criteria.
(c) Document the results of inspection and test.

3.2.3. Quality Records

The contractor shall:

(a) Maintain quality records as evidence that the items meet contractual requirements (inspection programme, procedures).
(b) Establish and maintain inspection and test records that identify as a minimum:

    (i)   The item inspected or tested.
   (ii)   The inspection or test performed, and the basis for acceptance of results.
  (iii)   The date of inspection or test.
  (iv)   The inspector or tester or data recorder.
   (v)   Non-conformances identified during inspection or test.

(c) Retain quality records for the time specified in the contract. If not specified, quality records defined in (b) shall be retained for 10 years.
(d) Submit the certificates of conformance along with shipments.

3.2.4. Non-conformances

The contractor is responsible for the disposition of all non-conforming items. Final acceptance of the contractor's disposition of those items that violate contractual requirements is the prerogative of the customer.
    The contractor shall:

(a) Detect and record non-conformances except if corrected immediately in accordance with common manufacturing practices.
(b) Identify and hold non-conforming items for evaluation; these need not be held if subsequent work is not affected.
(c) Develop a disposition that has the concurrence of all responsible parties.
(d) Implement the accepted disposition. This shall include requirements for re-inspecting and retesting repaired and reworked items.
(e) Verify the implementation of accepted dispositions.
(f) Maintain records that identify non-conforming items, the nature and extent of non-conformance, its disposition and objective evidence that repaired and reworked items have been re-inspected or retested according to initial requirements.

3.2.5. Customer-supplied Items

The customer is responsible for specifying in the contract the Quality Management Requirements applicable for items supplied by himself to the contractor and for certifying that these items are consistent with the quality requirements of the final item.

The contractor shall:

(a) Verify customer certification.
(b) Examine customer-supplied items on receipt for completeness and proper type and to detect transit damage. Further receiving inspection is not required unless the contractor needs actual characteristics for subsequent work or unless specified in the contract. Examination may be deferred until further processing is scheduled if items are in sealed containers or have special preservation or packaging.
(c) Report promptly in writing to the quality assurance representative any customer-supplied items found damaged, lost, non-conforming, or otherwise unsuitable or unnecessary for use either on receipt or while in the contractor's custody.
(d) Protect customer-supplied items against damage during storage and handling.

4. VERIFICATION OF QUALITY

4.1. ACCESS

If specified in the contract, the contractor shall provide for reasonable access of the customer to his premises and records for surveillance purposes.

Quality Management Requirements M3

Contents

1. SCOPE   96

1.1. General   96
1.2. Applicability   96
1.3. Contractor's Responsibilities   96

2. DEFINITIONS   96

3. REQUIREMENTS   96

3.1. Basic Requirements   96
3.2. Specific Requirements   97
3.2.1. Measuring and Testing Equipment   97
3.2.2. Inspection and Test   97
3.2.3. Quality Records   97
3.2.4. Non-conformances   97

4. VERIFICATION OF QUALITY   97

4.1. Access   97

1. SCOPE

1.1. GENERAL

This chapter specifies requirements to be complied with by the contractor to ensure an efficient quality management in manufacturing.

1.2. APPLICABILITY

The requirements of this chapter apply to the manufacturing of items, when specified in a contract.

1.3. CONTRACTOR'S RESPONSIBILITIES

The contractor's responsibilities are:

(a) To detect and dispose of non-conformances to contractual requirements.
(b) To comply with the customer's requirements as specified in the contract.
(c) To produce objective evidence that items meet contractual requirements
(d) To initiate corrective measures promptly when the quality assurance representative notifies the contractor of deviations from established requirements.

2. DEFINITIONS

Refer to Quality Management Directive.

3. REQUIREMENTS

3.1. BASIC REQUIREMENTS

Not applicable.

3.2. SPECIFIC REQUIREMENTS

3.2.1. *Measuring and Testing Equipment*

No special calibration and control measures are necessary on rulers, tape measures, levels and other such devices, if normal commercial practices provide for adequate accuracy and/or if large tolerances are allowed for the corresponding measurements.

In all other cases, the contractor shall provide objective evidence that measuring and testing equipment can provide for valid measurements.

3.2.2. *Inspection and Test*

The contractor shall inspect and test the items as necessary and document the results.

3.2.3. *Quality Records*

The contractor shall establish and maintain inspection and test records.

3.2.4. *Non-conformances*

The contractor shall detect and disposition all non-conforming items. Final acceptance of the contractor's disposition of those items that violate contractual requirements is the prerogative of the customer.

4. VERIFICATION OF QUALITY

4.1. ACCESS

If specified in the contract, the contractor shall provide for reasonable access of the customer to his premises and records for surveillance purposes.

Quality Management Requirements C1

Contents

1. SCOPE   101

1.1. General   101
1.2. Applicability   101
1.3. Contractor's Responsibilities   101

2. DEFINITIONS   102

3. REQUIREMENTS   102

3.1. Basic Requirements   102
3.1.1. Quality Assurance Programme   102
3.1.2. Organization   102
3.1.3. Quality Assurance Documents   104
3.1.3.1. Quality Assurance Manual   104
3.1.3.2. Quality Plan   105
3.1.3.3. Quality Assurance Procedures   106
3.2. Specific Requirements   107
3.2.1. Design Management   107
3.2.2. Document Control   107
3.2.3. Procurement   108
3.2.3.1. Selection of Subcontractors   108
3.2.3.2. Subcontract Requirements   108
3.2.3.3. Amendments to Subcontracts   109
3.2.3.4. Verification of the Quality Management System Implemented by a Subcontractor   109
3.2.3.5. Receiving Inspection   109
3.2.4. Measuring and Testing Equipment   110
3.2.5. Inspection and Test   111
3.2.6. In-process Inspection   111
3.2.7. Final Inspection   112
3.2.8. Inspection Status   112
3.2.9. Identification and Traceability   113
3.2.10. Preservation, Handling and Storage   113

3.2.11. Construction   114
3.2.12. Special Processes   114
3.2.13. Packaging and Shipping   115
3.2.14. Quality Records   115
3.2.15. Non-conformances   116
3.2.16. Customer-supplied Items   117
3.2.17. Corrective Action   118
3.2.18. Audits   118

4.   VERIFICATION OF QUALITY   119

4.1.   Initial Evaluation   119
4.1.1.   Quality Assurance Programme, Facilities and
         Physical Resources   119
4.1.2.   Quality Plan   119
4.2.   Continuing Evaluation and Verification   120
4.3.   Access   120

1. SCOPE

1.1. GENERAL

This chapter specifies requirements to be incorporated in a contractor's quality assurance programme for construction. The contractor is responsible for planning and developing a programme that assures that all his management, design and technical responsibilities for quality are incorporated and executed effectively. The programme is aimed primarily at ensuring an efficient quality management in construction and taking corrective actions, when necessary.

Planning and detailed written procedures are essential for specifying how such activities as the following, which affect quality, are to be performed and controlled:

(a) Design management.
(b) Procurement.
(c) Construction.
(d) Special processes.
(e) Measuring and testing equipment.
(f) Inspection and testing.
(g) Handling, storing, preservation, packaging and shipping.
(h) Item identification and traceability.
(i) Documentation and quality records.
(j) Disposition of non-conformances and corrective action.
(k) Quality audits and management reviews.

1.2. APPLICABILITY

The requirements of this chapter apply to construction activities when specified in a contract.

The requirements are valid for general civil construction activities. For concreting activities, a specific interpretation is given in some clauses.

1.3. CONTRACTOR'S RESPONSIBILITIES

The contractor's responsibilities are:

(a) To develop and implement the controls and quality assurance procedures specified herein that will promptly detect and dispose of, or prevent, non-conformances to contractual requirements.

(b) To comply with the customer's requirements as specified in the contract.

(c) To prepare a quality assurance manual which shall be submitted for the customer's concurrence before the contract is awarded or at the latest before the works start, as required in 3.1.3.1.

(d) To prepare a quality plan which shall be submitted to the customer before the works start, as required in 3.1.3.2.

(e) To update and resubmit the quality assurance manual and quality plan to reflect current practices when significant changes occur in the contractor's programme or organization in order to improve its effectiveness or to prevent recurrence of non-conformances.

(f) To initiate corrective measures promptly when the quality assurance representative notifies the contractor of deviations from established requirements.

2. DEFINITIONS

Refer to Quality Management Directive.

3. REQUIREMENTS

3.1. BASIC REQUIREMENTS

3.1.1. *Quality Assurance Programme*

The contractor shall plan, establish, implement, and maintain a quality assurance programme that complies with the requirements of this chapter.

3.1.2. *Organization*

The contractor shall:

(a) Clearly define management policies, objectives and responsibilities for quality assurance, including the responsibility of each division within a multi-divisional organization. The responsibility and authority for quality of those managing and performing the work and of those auditing and verifying conformance to quality requirements shall be defined and their relationships shown on organization charts.

(b) Provide for the review by management of the status and adequacy of the quality assurance programme.

(c) Appoint a representative who shall report regularly to management at a level that ensures that quality assurance requirements are not subordinated to design, manufacturing, construction, or delivery and define his authority to resolve quality matters. The customer shall be notified of the appointment in writing.

(d) Define the responsibility and authority of personnel who are primarily responsible for quality assurance and their organizational independence during audits and define the responsibility and authority of personnel who are primarily responsible for quality control and their organizational independence to:

    (i)   identify and record quality problems
    (ii)   initiate or recommend or provide solutions through designated channels
    (iii) verify the implementation of dispositions
    (iv)   control further processing, delivery or installation of a non-conforming item or service until the deficiency or unsatisfactory condition has been resolved.

Note that, generally, audit personnel shall not be within the pattern of daily activities.

(e) Use competent persons for inspection, other than those performing or directly supervising the work being inspected unless specifically designated otherwise in the quality plan. Such persons shall report to an adequate level of management, excluding direct report to supervisors responsible for producing the work being inspected.

Generally, inspectors shall verify the conformance to specifications and drawings. In cases of problems or difficulties, they shall request clarifications from the design or other competent organizations and initiate appropriate measures.

If examinations, being a part of the whole inspections, are performed and documented by works personnel, the extent of the inspections by the independent personnel may be reduced, if such has been provided for by the quality plan.

3.1.3. *Quality Assurance Documents*

3.1.3.1. *Quality Assurance Manual*
(a) The contractor shall:

    (i) Prepare a quality assurance manual, approved and signed by a senior management official, and submit it for the customer's concurrence before the contract is awarded or at the latest before the works start. A quality assurance manual submitted under a previous contract or tender document may be referred to.

    (ii) Review and update the manual to reflect current quality assurance policies and procedures and resubmit the resulting manual.

    (iii) Implement the programme according to the provisions specified in the manual.

(b) The quality assurance manual shall deal as appropriate with the following:

    (i) Organization — The manual shall define the organizational measures as specified in 3.1.2.

    (ii) Quality plan — The manual shall identify the group responsible for the quality plan specified in 3.1.3.2. and define its main principles and features in adequate procedures.

    (iii) Quality assurance procedures — Documented QA procedures as specified in 3.1.3.3. shall be included or shall be outlined and cross-referenced. Referenced QA procedures shall be made available to the quality assurance representative.

    (iv) Manual review — A statement shall be incorporated for reviewing and updating the manual as specified in 3.1.3.1.(a)(ii).

3.1.3.2. *Quality Plan*

(a) The contractor shall:

    (i)   Plan the inspection and test activities.

    (ii) Identify in the quality plan the inspections and tests to be performed on the items listed in the contract in compliance with contractual and/or technical requirements.

    (iii) Submit the plan for the customer's concurrence following the award of the contract and before the work starts. Referenced inspection and test specifications and/or procedures shall be made available to the quality assurance representative during the implementation of the quality plan.

    (iv) Update the plan during the life of the contract to reflect current conditions of manufacturing, construction, inspecting and testing and resubmit the plan to the customer.

(b) The quality plan may be of any format to suit the contractor's system. The quality plan shall deal as appropriate with:

    (i)   Identification of the characteristics or items to be inspected and tested.

    (ii) Identification of required inspection, test and special process operations and their relative location in the construction cycle. The contractor may include additional in-process inspection points for his own evaluation of quality which will not be subject to acceptance and witness by the quality assurance representative.

    (iii) Reference of inspection, test and special process procedures, standards, acceptance criteria and sampling plan, if any.

      (iv) Indication of hold points beyond which the activity shall not proceed until the required inspections or tests have shown satisfactory results and have been documented.

      (v) Provisions for the customer to insert witness points at which activities are to be observed. The activity may nevertheless proceed beyond a witness point, should the customer fail to attend in spite of due notification.

(c) The quality plans for subcontracted items or services, when concurred with by the contractor, shall be submitted to the customer, as applicable, for concurrence and insertion of witness points.

3.1.3.3. *Quality Assurance Procedures*

The contractor shall have procedures for the following specific requirements if they apply to the contract:

Design management	Clause 3.2.1.
Document control	Clause 3.2.2.
Procurement	Clause 3.2.3.
Measuring and testing equipment	Clause 3.2.4.
Inspection and test	Clause 3.2.5.
In-process inspection	Clause 3.2.6.
Final inspection	Clause 3.2.7.
Inspection status	Clause 3.2.8.
Identification and traceability	Clause 3.2.9.
Preservation, handling and storage	Clause 3.2.10.
Construction	Clause 3.2.11.
Special processes	Clause 3.2.12.
Quality records	Clause 3.2.14.
Non-conformances	Clause 3.2.15.
Customer-supplied items	Clause 3.2.16.
Corrective action	Clause 3.2.17.
Audits	Clause 3.2.18.

Each QA procedure shall define, as applicable, such things as: its purpose and scope; who is responsible for what; how all steps are to be performed; what materials, equipment and documentation are to be used; how it is all controlled.

Forms used shall be exhibited.

QA procedures shall be updated when necessary.

3.2. SPECIFIC REQUIREMENTS

3.2.1. *Design Management*

Refer to chapter D1, D2 or D3 as applicable.

3.2.2. *Document Control*

The contractor shall:

(a) Establish measures to ensure that all essential quality related documents, including but not limited to those listed below, are reviewed for adequacy and approved for release by authorized personnel:

    (i) Quality assurance manual required by 3.1.3.1.
    (ii) Quality plan required by 3.1.3.2.
    (iii) Quality assurance procedures required by 3.1.3.3.
    (iv) Design documents as a consequence of 3.2.1.
    (v) Procurement documents required by 3.2.3.
    (vi) Calibration procedures required by 3.2.4.
    (vii) Inspection and test procedures required by 3.2.5.
    (viii) Construction documents required by 3.2.11.
    (ix) Special process procedures required by 3.2.12.

(b) Establish distribution lists for the above-mentioned documents, and update and maintain them in the current form to assure that the relevant personnel are issued with all the documents necessary to perform the work.

(c) Make the applicable issues of these documents available at areas where these activities are performed.

(d) Establish and update lists of applicable documents for construction and distribute them systematically. Controlled distribution is required for these lists only.

(e) Ensure that changes to documents receive the authorizations by the same organizations as the initial documents unless other organizations are specifically designated. Maintain a record of changes as they are made. Written notes on documents are acceptable provided that they are made by authorized persons according to established procedures. Documents shall be revised and re-issued after a practical number of changes have been issued.

(f) Process field changes to design documents (drawings, specifications) in accordance with a specific field change procedure that clearly defines the responsibility for changes approval, delegation of this responsibility and the limit of this delegation with regard to the importance (degree) of changes.

3.2.3. Procurement

3.2.3.1. Selection of Subcontractors

The contractor shall identify items and services to be procured.

He shall undertake the following:

(a) Determine for these subcontracted items and services the applicable Quality Management Requirements. Classification to these Quality Management Requirements shall be in such a way that the overall quality is not impaired. The classification list shall be submitted to the customer for acceptance.

(b) Evaluate and select subcontractors in accordance with 4.1. of the applicable Quality Management Requirements with regard to their ability to meet subcontract and quality requirements.

(c) When 'off the shelf' items are to be procured, evaluation of subcontractor may not necessarily be required. The contractor shall nominate to the quality assurance representative those materials and items that belong to this category.

3.2.3.2. Subcontract Requirements

The contractor shall include in subcontracts the following as applicable:

(a) A clear description of the items or services to be procured including technical data and inspection and test requirements by reference to standards, technical specifications, drawings, etc.

(b) A designation of the Quality Management Requirements to be applied to the items or services and exceptions, if any.

(c) A designation of the contractor's QA procedures to

be implemented by the subcontractor, if applicable.
(d) Instructions for the submission, retention and disposition of quality records.
(e) Requirements for packaging and shipping where applicable.
(f) A statement related to the right of access to the subcontractor's premises and records for audits and/or surveillance by the contractor or the customer.
(g) Instructions for notification of witness points.
(h) Requirements for the subcontractor to report non-conformances.
(i) Applicable requirements to be extended to lower tier subcontractors.

Subcontract documents shall be reviewed and approved in accordance with 3.2.2.(a).

All unpriced subcontracts and associated reference data shall be made available on request for review by the quality assurance representative.

3.2.3.3.   Amendments to Subcontracts
The contractor shall process amendments to subcontracts in the same way as the initial subcontract and reference the initial subcontract number in the amendments.

3.2.3.4.   Verification of the Quality Management System Implemented by a Subcontractor.
Refer to 4.2. of the applicable Quality Management Requirements.

3.2.3.5.   Receiving Inspection
To the extent that is practical, receiving inspection shall be specified in the quality plan.
The contractor shall:

(a) Identify and inspect items on receipt to ascertain that they comply with contractual requirements. In determining the amount or nature of receiving inspection, consideration shall be given to the surveillance exercised at source and documented evidence of quality conformance. Receiving inspection shall cover as a minimum: verification of deterioration or damage during transport, identification control, review of required documentation.

(b) Initiate corrective action with subcontractors when non-conforming items are received, as required by the nature and frequency of non-conformances.

(c) Hold incoming items until the required inspection and/or test have been completed or the necessary inspection and/or test reports have been received and verified, except when items are released under positive recall.

3.2.4. *Measuring and Testing Equipment*

All measuring and testing equipment and devices used to verify characteristics that can affect item quality shall be controlled and maintained. At prescribed intervals, or prior to use, they shall be calibrated and adjusted against certified equipment having a known valid relationship to nationally recognized standards. Where no national standards exist, the basis employed for calibration shall be documented.

No special calibration and control measures are necessary on rulers, tape measures, levels and other such devices, if normal commercial practices provide for adequate accuracy or if large tolerances are allowed for the corresponding measurements.

The contractor shall:

(a) Include in calibration procedures: equipment type, frequency of checks, description of check method, acceptance criteria and action to be taken when results are unsatisfactory. Exceptions will be allowed for measuring and testing equipment for which calibration is simple and does not require a specific detailed procedure. The contractor shall identify those types of measuring equipment for which he has not provided documented calibration procedures.

(b) Identify measuring and testing equipment with a tag, sticker, or other suitable indicator to show the calibration status.

(c) Maintain calibration records for measuring and testing equipment.

(d) Assess and document the validity of previous inspection and test results when measuring and testing equipment are found to be out of calibration.

For concreting and earthwork activities:

(e)   The above-mentioned requirements are mandatorily applicable only to the following equipment and instruments:

— laboratory scale
— concrete batching plant
— compression test machine
— tensile test machine
— prestressing pressure gauge
— soil–cement batching plant
— gauge for mechanical splicing
— grout batching machine.

For all other equipment and instruments, the requirements are non-mandatory but they may be used as a guide.

3.2.5.   Inspection and Test

(a)   The contractor shall provide for the performance of inspections and tests as specified in the quality plan. These inspections and tests shall be carried out in accordance with written procedures that define the method, the materials, instruments or equipment to be used and acceptance/rejection criteria.
The contractor shall amend the selected inspection methods in cases where their unsuitability is demonstrated.

(b)   Inspections and tests shall be documented on inspection and test reports that identify as a minimum the item inspected or tested, applicable drawings, specifications or procedures, the date of inspection or test, the inspector, tester or data recorder, the type of observation, the results, the acceptability and the action taken in connection with any deficiencies identified.

3.2.6.   In-process Inspection

The contractor shall:

(a)   Identify, inspect and/or test items as required by the quality plan.

(b)   Monitor process methods, where inspection is not feasible.

(c)   Hold items until the required inspections and/or tests have been completed or necessary reports have been received and verified except when items are released under positive recall. Release under positive recall shall not preclude (a) above.

For concreting activities:

(i)   The contractor shall establish adequate measures for preconcreting, in-process and post-concreting inspections to be performed as applicable.

(ii)   A part of these inspections and the documentation thereof may be delegated to the works personnel. In such cases, the independent inspections can be reduced to an extent to be defined in the quality plan or in the inspection procedures.

This applies particularly to the case where a specialist is incorporated into the work staff for difficult or sophisticated tasks such as reinforcement placing, prestressing, etc.

(iii) Such measures do not preclude complete independent inspections to be performed on a programmed basis or as a consequence of results obtained.

3.2.7.   Final Inspection

The contractor shall:

(a)   Identify, inspect and/or test the final items as required by the quality plan.

(b)   Verify that the items have been inspected at all points shown in the quality plan and that the records are adequate and complete.

3.2.8.   Inspection Status

The contractor shall:

(a)   Provide means for assuring that required inspections and tests are performed and that the acceptability of items with regard to inspections and tests performed is known throughout manufacturing and construction.

(b) Establish and maintain a system for identifying the inspection/acceptance status by means of tags, stamped impressions or other physical means to be affixed to the item or its container or by means of inspection records.

(c) Show the identity of the contractor and his inspector on any inspection marking used.

(d) Provide for measures for controlling status indicators including the authority for application and removal of tags, stamps or other marking.

(e) Identify non-conforming items.

3.2.9. Identification and Traceability

The contractor shall establish and maintain an adequate system to :

(a) Identify each item (lot, component or part) to the applicable drawing, specification or other technical document, throughout the whole construction process.

(b) Assign to each item a unique identification where specific traceability is required by the contract.

(c) Record this identification on all process, inspection and test records, where traceability is specified.

(d) List the items that do or do not require traceability concerning concreting activities.

3.2.10. Preservation, Handling and Storage

The contractor shall:

(a) Establish, maintain and document a system for the preservation, storage and handling of all items from the time of receipt through the entire construction process and subsequent storage to prevent abuse, misuse, damage, deterioration or loss.

(b) Periodically inspect stored items for condition and shelf-life expiry.

(c) Inspect and test special handling tools and equipment at specific times to verify that the tools and equipment are adequately maintained and will not damage the

items and will ensure safe and adequate handling.
(d) Use specific written procedures for lifting of critical or high value items.

3.2.11. Construction

(a) The contractor shall clearly define the responsibilities for the documented preparation of works.

This written preparation shall consist of instructions or work assignments. It shall be established in accordance with the construction schedules and be available to the works and inspection personnel prior to commencement of work. This work instruction will document the following:

— work methods
— sequence of operations
— workmanship criteria
— type of equipment needed
— special working environment, if any.

For concreting and other common civil work activities, these instructions may be included in drawings, specifications or other design documents.
(b) The contractor shall ensure that prior to release for construction all jigs, fixtures, tooling masters, templates, and patterns used for verifying quality are controlled. The extent and frequency of tool control shall be defined.

3.2.12. Special Processes

The contractor shall:

(a) Identify those special processes subject to the requirements of this clause. Special processes shall include welding, heat treating and non-destructive examination, as applicable.
(b) Establish documented procedures to assure that these processes are accomplished under controlled conditions by qualified personnel using qualified documented procedures and suitable equipment in accordance with applicable codes, standards, specifications, criteria and contractual requirements.

(c)   Maintain documentation for currently qualified personnel and processes according to the requirements of pertinent codes and standards.

(d)   Define the necessary qualifications of personnel and procedures for special processes not covered by existing codes or standards, or where item or service quality requirements exceed the requirements of established codes or standards.

(e)   Include special processes in the quality plan.

(f)   Not consider concreting as a special process. However, the contractor shall ensure that foremen and vibration operators are properly selected from experienced or trained personnel prior to assignment of works and are given regular training by concrete placement experts as needed.

3.2.13. *Packaging and Shipping*

Not applicable.

3.2.14. *Quality Records*

The contractor shall:

(a)   Maintain quality records as evidence that:

  (i)   The quality assurance programme meets the requirements of these Quality Management Requirements (manual, procedures, quality plan).

  (ii)   The items or services meet contractual or other applicable technical requirements (specifications, drawings, calculations, construction, inspection and test procedures).

  (iii)   Personnel and procedures for special processes are qualified as required by 3.2.12(c).

  (iv)   Measuring and testing equipment are calibrated as required by 3.2.4.

  (v)   The procurements meet the requirements of 3.2.3.

  (vi)   Corrective actions are being taken and are effective as required by 3.2.17.

  (vii)   Audits are performed as required by 3.2.18.

(b)   Maintain final performance quality records which include as appropriate:

      (i)   as-built records
     (ii)   material test reports or certificates
   (iii) non-destructive examination records or certificates
   (iv) inspection and test records
    (v) non-conformance reports
   (vi) concrete batch plant printout.

Items (iii) and (iv) apply to those operations performed after receipt of materials from the supplier.

(c)   Identify, index and file quality records for easy retrieval.

(d)   Retain quality records for the time specified in the contract. If not specified final performance quality records shall be retained for 10 years.

(e)   Provide a suitable environment for storing of records to minimize deterioration or damage and to prevent loss (the use of a double filing system is an acceptable method).

3.2.15. *Non-conformances*

The contractor is responsible for the identification and disposition of all non-conforming items, including those of subcontractors. Final acceptance of the contractor's disposition of those items that violate contractual requirements is the prerogative of the customer.

The contractor shall:

(a)   Establish and maintain measures for controlling non-conforming items that:

    (i)   Define the responsibility and authority of those who dispose of non-conforming items. This shall include provision for a technical review that involves those who are responsible for design, manufacturing, construction and quality functions, if these functions are concerned.

   (ii)   Detect and record non-conformances promptly except if corrected immediately in accordance with common construction practices.

  (iii) Identify and hold non-conforming items for

evaluation; these need not be held if the
subsequent work is not affected.

(iv)   Develop a disposition that has the concurrence
of all responsible parties.

(v)   Implement the accepted disposition. This shall
include requirements for re-inspecting and
retesting repaired and reworked items.

(vi)   Verify the implementation of accepted
dispositions.

(b)   Provide for holding areas or methods for segregating
non-conforming items to prevent unauthorized use,
shipment, or mixing with conforming items.
However, where physical segregation is not practical
or the non-conformance is not clearly visible, tagging,
marking or other positive means of identification are
acceptable.

(c)   Maintain records that identify non-conforming items,
the nature and extent of non-conformance, its
disposition, and objective evidence that repaired and
reworked items have been re-inspected or retested
according to applicable procedures.

3.2.16. *Customer-supplied Items*

The customer is responsible for specifying in the contract
the Quality Management Requirements applicable for
items supplied by himself to the contractors and for
certifying that these items are consistent with the quality
requirements of the final work.

The contractor shall:

(a)   Verify customer certification.

(b)   Examine customer-supplied items on receipt for
completeness and proper type and to detect transit
damage. Further receiving inspection is not required
unless the contractor needs actual characteristics for
subsequent work or unless specified in the contract.
Examination may be deferred until further processing
is scheduled if items are in sealed containers or have
special preservation or packaging.

(c)   Control customer-supplied items from receipt
onwards according to the requirements of this
standard.

(d)   Report promptly in writing to the quality assurance representative any customer-supplied items found damaged, lost, non-conforming, or otherwise unsuitable or unnecessary for use either on receipt or while in the contractor's custody.

3.2.17. Corrective Action

The contractor shall:

(a)   Investigate the causes of significant or recurring non-conformances and take appropriate actions to prevent repetition.

(b)   Document and have reported to appropriate levels of the contractor's management causes of significant conditions adversely affecting quality and the corrective actions taken.

3.2.18. Audits

(a)   The contractor shall establish, implement and document a plan for audits which objectively evaluates and verifies that:

    (i)   He is complying with all aspects of his quality assurance programme, documented quality programme procedures, and specified requirements.

    (ii)   The quality assurance programme is performing adequately.

    (iii)   Recommended corrective actions are being implemented effectively.

    (iv)   Deficient areas are being re-audited.

(b)   The audit plan shall define:

    (i)   Functional areas to be audited.

    (ii)   Assignments of those performing the audits.

    (iii)   Frequency of audits.

    (iv)   Methods for reporting findings and recommendations.

    (v)   The means for having corrective actions initiated and implemented.

(c)   Audits shall include an evaluation of:

    (i)   Work areas, activities, processes, items and services being produced.

    (ii)   Quality assurance practices, documented procedures. and instructions.

    (iii)   Documents and records.

(d) Appropriately trained personnel who are not directly responsible for the area being audited shall perform the audits according to documented audit procedures or check-lists that identify the essential characteristics to be verified; all auditors shall be cognizant of the field being audited.

(e) Management responsible for the area audited shall review and correct deficiencies identified in the documented audit results.

4. VERIFICATION OF QUALITY

4.1. INITIAL EVALUATION

4.1.1. *Quality Assurance Programme, Facilities and Physical Resources*

Prior to the award of a contract and/or prior to the time of performing the works the customer shall evaluate the contractor's quality assurance programme, construction facilities and resources to determine whether the requirements of this chapter can be met.

In the event of the contractor not fulfilling all applicable requirements, the customer may award the contract provided that he takes the responsibility for those QA requirements that will not be met by the contractor. In such a case, the exceptions shall be clearly defined in the contract.

4.1.2. *Quality Plan*

The customer shall evaluate the quality plan and all revisions thereto in order to determine its acceptability.

The customer shall indicate his witness point on the accepted quality plan.

4.2.   CONTINUING EVALUATION AND VERIFICATION

The schedule or frequency of the customer's and authorities' audits should be outlined in the contract.

If not otherwise specified in the contract, a maximum of one audit will be performed each year.

In addition, the customer shall perform surveillances according to the accepted quality plan.

4.3.   ACCESS

The contractor shall provide for reasonable access of the competent authorities and of the customer to his premises and records for audit and surveillance purposes.

Quality Management Requirements C2

Contents

1.	SCOPE	123
1.1.	General	123
1.2.	Applicability	123
1.3.	Contractor's Responsibilities	124
2.	DEFINITIONS	124
3.	REQUIREMENTS	124
3.1.	Basic Requirements	124
3.1.1.	Quality Assurance Programme	124
3.1.2.	Organization	124
3.1.3.	Quality Assurance Documents	126
3.1.3.1.	Quality Assurance Manual	126
3.1.3.2.	Quality Plan	127
3.1.3.3.	Quality Assurance Procedures	128
3.2.	Specific Requirements	128
3.2.1.	Design Management	128
3.2.2.	Document Control	128
3.2.3.	Procurement	129
3.2.3.1.	Selection of Subcontractors	129
3.2.3.2.	Subcontract Requirements	130
3.2.3.3.	Amendments to Subcontracts	130
3.2.3.4.	Verification of the Quality Management System Implemented by a Subcontractor	131
3.2.3.5.	Receiving Inspection	131
3.2.4.	Measuring and Testing Equipment	131
3.2.5.	Inspection and Test	132
3.2.6.	In-process Inspection	133
3.2.7.	Final Inspection	133
3.2.8.	Inspection Status	134
3.2.9.	Identification and Traceability	134
3.2.10.	Preservation, Handling and Storage	134

3.2.11. Construction   135
3.2.12. Special Processes   135
3.2.13. Packaging and Shipping   136
3.2.14. Quality Records   136
3.2.15. Non-conformances   137
3.2.16. Customer-supplied Items   138

4.   VERIFICATION OF QUALITY   139

4.1.   Initial Evaluation   139
4.1.1.   Quality Assurance Programme, Facilities and
           Physical Resources   139
4.1.2. Quality Plan   139
4.2.   Continuing Evaluation and Verification   139
4.3.   Access   139

5.   ATTACHMENT: SUMMARY OF THE
     REQUIREMENTS   140

1. SCOPE

1.1. GENERAL

This chapter specifies requirements to be incorporated in a contractor's quality assurance programme for construction. The contractor is responsible for planning and developing a programme that assures that all his management and technical responsibilities for quality are incorporated and executed effectively. The programme is aimed primarily at ensuring an efficient quality management in construction.

Planning and detailed written procedures are essential for specifying how such activities as the following, which affect quality, are to be performed and controlled:

(a) Design management.
(b) Procurement.
(c) Construction.
(d) Special processes.
(e) Measuring and testing equipment.
(f) Inspection and testing.
(g) Handling, storing, preservation, packaging and shipping.
(h) Item identification and traceability.
(i) Documentation and quality records.
(j) Disposition of non-conformances.

1.2. APPLICABILITY

The requirements of this chapter apply to construction activities when specified in a contract.

The requirements are valid for general civil construction activities. However, where concreting activities are the most important part of civil works, a specific interpretation is given in some clauses.

The mandatory requirements (identified as M in the left-hand margin) are always applicable to the contractor if the contractual documents refer to this section C2.

In addition to these mandatory requirements, optional requirements (identified as O in the left-hand margin) will be applicable if specifically addressed in the contractual documents.

1.3.   CONTRACTOR'S RESPONSIBILITIES

The contractor's responsibilities are:

(a)   To develop and implement the controls and, if required, quality assurance procedures specified herein that will promptly detect and correct non-conformances to contractual requirements.

(b)   To comply with the customer's requirements as specified in the contract.

(c)   To prepare a quality assurance manual which shall be submitted to the customer at the latest before the works start, as required in 3.1.3.1.

(d)   To prepare a quality plan which shall be submitted to the customer before the works start, as required in 3.1.3.2.

(e)   To update and resubmit the quality assurance manual and quality plan to reflect current practices when significant changes occur in the contractor's programme or organization in order to improve its effectiveness.

(f)   To initiate corrective measures promptly when the quality assurance representative notifies the contractor of deviations from established requirements.

2. DEFINITIONS

Refer to Quality Management Directive.

3. REQUIREMENTS

3.1. BASIC REQUIREMENTS

3.1.1. *Quality Assurance Programme*

M   The contractor shall plan, establish, implement and maintain a quality assurance programme that complies with the requirements of this chapter.

3.1.2. *Organization*

The contractor shall:

M   (a)   Clearly define management policies, objectives and responsibilities for quality assurance including the responsibility of each division within a multi-divisional organization.

M   (b)   Appoint a representative who shall report regularly to management at a level that ensures that quality assurance requirements are not subordinated to design, manufacturing, construction, or delivery and define his authority to resolve quality matters.

O   (c)   Use competent persons for inspection, other than those performing or directly supervising the work being inspected, unless specifically designated otherwise in the quality plan.

Generally, inspectors shall verify the conformance to the specifications and drawings. In cases of problems or difficulties, they shall request clarifications from the design or other competent organizations and initiate appropriate measures.

If examinations being a part of the whole inspection are performed and documented by works personnel, the extent of the inspections by the independent personnel may be reduced, if such is provided for by the quality plan.

O   (d)   Define the responsibility and authority for quality of those managing and performing the work and of those verifying conformance to quality requirements, and show their relationships on organization charts.

O   (e)   Define the responsibility and authority of personnel who are primarily responsible for quality control and their organizational freedom to:

      (i)   Identify and record quality problems.
      (ii)   Initiate or recommend or provide solutions through designated channels.
      (iii)   Verify the implementation of dispositions.
      (iv)   Control further processing, delivery or installation of a non-conforming item or service until the deficiency or unsatisfactory condition has been resolved.

O   (f)   Assure that the inspection and quality control personnel report to an adequate level of management, excluding direct report to supervisors responsible for producing the work being inspected.

3.1.3.   *Quality Assurance Documents*

3.1.3.1.   *Quality Assurance Manual*

M   (a)   The contractor shall:

  (i)   Prepare a quality assurance manual, approved and signed by a senior management official.
  (ii)   Review and update the manual to reflect current quality assurance policies and procedures.
  (iii) Implement the programme according to the provisions specified in the manual.

M   (b)   The quality assurance manual shall deal as appropriate with the following:

  (i)   Organization — The manual shall define the organizational measures as specified in 3.1.2.
  (ii)   Quality plan — The manual shall identify the group responsible for the quality plan specified in 3.1.3.2. and define its main principles and features in adequate procedures.
  (iii) Quality assurance procedures — Documented QA procedures as specified in 3.1.3.3. shall be included or shall be outlined and cross-referenced. Referenced QA procedures shall be made available to the quality assurance representative.
  (iv)   Manual review — A statement shall be incorporated for reviewing and updating the manual as specified in 3.1.3.1.(a)(ii).

O   (c)   The contractor shall:

  (i)   Submit the quality assurance manual for the customer's concurrence at the latest before the works start. A quality assurance manual submitted under a previous contract or tender may be referred to.
  (ii)   Resubmit the manual after updating.

3.1.3.2.   *Quality Plan*
M   (a)   The contractor shall:

    (i)   Plan the inspection and test activities.
    (ii)   Identify in the quality plan the inspections and tests to be performed on the items listed in the contract in compliance with contractual and/or technical requirements.
    (iii)   Submit the plan for the customer's concurrence following the award of the contract and before the work starts. Referenced inspection and test specifications and/or procedures shall be made available to the quality assurance representative during the implementation of the quality plan.
    (iv)   Update the plan during the life of the contract to reflect current conditions of construction, inspecting and testing and resubmit the plan to the customer.

M   (b)   The quality plan may be of any format to suit the contractor's system. The quality plan shall deal as appropriate with:

    (i)   Identification of the characteristics or items to be inspected and tested.
    (ii)   Identification of required inspection, test and special process operations and their relative location in the construction cycle. The contractor may include additional in-process inspection points for his own evaluation of quality, which will not be subject to acceptance and witness by the quality assurance representative.
    (iii)   Reference of inspection, test and special process procedures, standards, acceptance criteria and sampling plan, if any.
    (iv)   Indication of hold points beyond which the activity shall not proceed until the required inspections or tests have shown satisfactory results and have been documented.
    (v)   Provisions for the customer to insert witness points at which activities are to be observed. The activity may nevertheless proceed

beyond a witness point should the customer fail to attend in spite of due notification.

O   (c) The quality plans for subcontracted items or services, when concurred with by the contractor, shall be submitted to the customer, as applicable, for concurrence and insertion of witness points.

3.1.3.3. *Quality Assurance Procedures*

M   The contractor shall have procedures for the following specific requirements, if required in the corresponding clauses:

Design management	3.2.1.
Document control	3.2.2.
Procurement	3.2.3.
Measuring and testing equipment	3.2.4.
Inspection and test	3.2.5.
In-process inspection	3.2.6.
Final inspection	3.2.7.
Inspection status	3.2.8.
Identification and traceability	3.2.9.
Preservation, handling and storage	3.2.10.
Construction	3.2.11.
Special processes	3.2.12.
Quality records	3.2.14.
Non-conformances	3.2.15.
Customer-supplied items	3.2.16.

QA procedures shall be updated when necessary.

3.2. SPECIFIC REQUIREMENTS

3.2.1. *Design Management*

Refer to chapter D1, D2 or D3 as applicable.

3.2.2. *Document Control*

The contractor shall:

M   (a) Establish measures to ensure that all essential documents affecting quality including but not limited to those listed below are approved for release:

    (i)   Quality assurance manual required by 3.1.3.1.
    (ii)   Quality plan required by 3.1.3.2.
    (iii)   Quality assurance procedures required by 3.1.3.3.
    (iv)   Design documents as a consequence of 3.2.1.
    (v)   Procurement documents required by 3.2.3.
    (vi)   Calibration procedures if required by 3.2.4.
    (vii)   Inspection and test procedures required by 3.2.5.
    (viii)   Construction documents if required by 3.2.11.
    (ix)   Special process procedures required by 3.2.12.

O   (b)   Establish and update lists of applicable documents for construction and distribute them systematically.

O   (c)   Ensure that changes to documents receive the authorizations by the same organizations as the initial documents unless other organizations are specifically designated. Maintain a record of changes as they are made. Written notes on documents are acceptable provided that they are made by authorized persons according to established procedures.

M   (d)   Process field changes to design documents (drawings, specifications) in accordance with a specific field change procedure that defines clearly the responsibility for changes approval, delegation of this responsibility and the limit of this delegation with regard to the importance (degree) of changes.

3.2.3. Procurement

3.2.3.1. Selection of Subcontractors

The contractor shall identify items and services to be procured.

He shall undertake the following:

M   (a)   Determine for these subcontracted items and services the applicable Quality Management Requirements. Classification to these Quality Management Requirements shall be in such a way that the overall quality is not impaired. The classification list shall be submitted to the customer for acceptance.

O   (b)   Evaluate and select subcontractors in accordance with 4.1. of the applicable Quality Management Requirements with regard to their ability to meet subcontract and quality requirements.

O   (c)   When 'off the shelf' items are to be procured, evaluation of subcontractor may not necessarily be required. The contractor shall nominate to the quality assurance representative those materials and items that belong to this category.

3.2.3.2. *Subcontract Requirements*

The contactor shall include in subcontracts the following as applicable:

M   (a)   A clear description of the items or services to be procured including technical data and inspection and test requirements by reference to standards, technical specifications, drawings, etc.

M   (b)   A designation of the Quality Management Requirements to be applied to the items or services and exceptions, if any.

M   (c)   A designation of the contractor's QA procedures to be implemented by the subcontractor, if applicable.

M   (d)   Requirements for packaging and shipping as applicable.

O   (e)   Instructions for the submission, retention and disposition of quality records.

O   (f)   A statement related to the right of access to the subcontractor's premises and records for surveillance by the contractor or the customer.

O   (g)   Instructions for notification of witness points.

O   (h)   Requirements to have the subcontractor reporting non-conformances.

O   (i)   All unpriced subcontracts and associated reference data shall be available on request for review by the quality assurance representative.

M   (j)   Subcontract documents shall be approved in accordance with 3.2.2.(a).

3.2.3.3. *Amendments to Subcontracts*

M   The contractor shall process amendments to subcontracts in the same way as the initial subcontract and reference the initial subcontract number in the amendments.

3.2.3.4.   *Verification of the Quality Management System*
         Implemented by a Subcontractor
         Refer to 4.2. of the applicable Quality Management
         Requirements.

3.2.3.5.   *Receiving Inspection*
         The contractor shall:

M   (a)   Identify and inspect items on receipt to ascertain
               that they comply with contractual requirements. In
               determining the amount or nature of receiving
               inspection, consideration shall be given to the
               surveillance exercised at source and documented
               evidence of quality conformance. Receiving
               inspection shall cover as a minimum: verification of
               deterioration   or   damage   during   transport,
               identification   control,   review   of   required
               documentation.

O   (b)   Hold non-conforming incoming items until decision
               is made about disposition except when items are
               released under positive recall.

3.2.4.   *Measuring and Testing Equipment*

         No special calibration and control measures are necessary
         on rulers, tape measures, levels, and other such devices, if
         normal commercial practices provide adequate accuracy or
         if large tolerances are allowed for the corresponding
         measurements.
         Generally, the contractor shall provide objective
         evidence that measuring and testing equipment:

M   (a)   are in known state of calibration (if necessary) or
M   (b)   can provide valid measurements (measuring and
               testing equipment shall be calibrated or it shall be
               shown that valid measurements can be obtained).

         For concreting and earthwork activities:

M   (c)   The above mentioned requirements are mandatorily
               applicable only to the following equipment and
               instruments

               — laboratory scale
               — concrete batching plant

— compression test machine
— tensile test machine
— prestressing pressure gauge
— soil–cement batching plant
— gauge for mechanical splicing
— grout batching machine.

For all other equipment and instruments, they are non-mandatory but they may be used as a guide.

The contractor shall:

O   (d) Include in calibration procedures: equipment type, frequency of checks, description of check method, acceptance criteria and action to be taken when results are unsatisfactory.
O   (e) Identify measuring and testing equipment with a tag, sticker, or other suitable indicator to show the calibration status.
O   (f) Maintain calibration records for measuring and testing equipment.
O   (g) Assess and document the validity of previous inspection and test results when measuring and testing equipment are found to be out of calibration.

3.2.5. Inspection and Test

M   (a) The contractor shall provide for the performance of inspections and tests as specified in the quality plan. These inspections and tests shall be carried out in accordance with written procedures that define the method, the materials, instruments or equipment to be used and acceptance/rejection criteria.
        The contractor shall amend the selected inspection methods in cases where their unsuitability is demonstrated.
M   (b) Inspections and tests shall be documented on inspection and test reports that identify as a minimum the item inspected or tested, applicable drawings, specifications or procedures, the date of inspection or test, the inspector, tester or data recorder, the type of observation, the results, the acceptability and the action taken in connection with any deficiencies identified.

3.2.6. In-process Inspection

The contractor shall:

M (a) Identify, inspect and/or test items as required by the quality plan.

O (b) Monitor process methods, where inspection is not feasible.

O (c) Hold items until the required inspections and/or tests have been completed or necessary reports have been received and verified except when items are released under positive recall. Release under positive recall shall not preclude (a) above.

O (d) Establish a procedure if any optional requirements are specified in the contract.

For concreting activities:

(i) The contractor shall establish adequate measures for preconcreting, in-process and post-concreting inspections to be performed as applicable.

(ii) A part of these inspections and the documentation thereof may be delegated to the works personnel. In such a case, the independent inspections can be reduced to an extent to be defined in the quality plan.

This applies particularly to the case when a specialist is incorporated into the work staff for difficult or sophisticated tasks such as reinforcement placing, prestressing, etc.

(iii) Such measures do not preclude complete independent inspections to be performed on a programmed basis or as a consequence of results obtained.

3.2.7. Final Inspection

The contractor shall:

M (a) Identify, inspect and/or test the final items as required by the quality plan.

O (b) Verify that items have been inspected at all points shown in the quality plan and that the records are adequate and complete.

O (c) Establish a procedure.

3.2.8.   Inspection Status

The contractor shall:

O   (a)   Provide means for assuring that required inspections and tests are performed and that the acceptability of items with regard to inspections and tests performed is known throughout manufacturing and construction (for example, inspection records are sufficient evidence).

M   (b)   Identify non-conforming items.

3.2.9.   Identification and Traceability

The contractor shall establish and maintain an adequate system to:

O   (a)   Identify each item (lot, component or part) to the applicable drawing, specification or other technical document, throughout the whole construction process.

O   (b)   Assign to each item a unique identification where specific traceability is required by the contract.

O   (c)   Record this identification on all process, inspection and test records, where traceability is specified.

M   (d)   List the items that do or do not require traceability concerning concreting activities.

3.2.10. Preservation, Handling and Storage

The contractor shall:

O   (a)   Establish, maintain and document a system for the preservation, storage and handling of all items from the time of receipt through the entire construction process and subsequent storage to prevent abuse, misuse, damage, deterioration or loss.

O   (b)   Periodically inspect stored items for conditions and shelf-life expiry.

O   (c)   Inspect and test special handling tools and equipment at specific times to verify that the tools and equipment are adequately maintained and will not damage the items and will ensure safe and adequate handling.

O   (d)   Use specific written procedures for lifting of critical or high value items.

3.2.11. Construction

O   (a)   The contractor shall clearly define the responsibility for the documented preparation of works.

This written preparation shall consist of instructions or work assignments. It shall be established in accordance with the construction schedules and be available to the works and inspection personnel prior to commencement of work. These work instructions will document the following:

— work methods
— sequence of operations
— workmanship criteria
— type of equipment needed
— special working environment, if any.

For concreting and other common civil work activities, these instructions may be included in drawings, specifications or other design documents.

O   (b)   The contractor shall ensure that prior to release for construction, all jigs, fixtures, tooling masters, templates, and patterns used for verifying quality are controlled. The extent and frequency of tool control shall be defined.

3.2.12. Special Processes

The contractor shall:

M   (a)   Identify those special processes subject to the requirements of this clause. Special processes shall include as applicable welding, heat treating and non-destructive examination.

M   (b)   Include special processes in the quality plan.

O   (c)   Establish documented procedures to assure that these processes are accomplished under controlled conditions by qualified personnel using qualified documented procedures and suitable equipment in accordance with applicable codes, standards, specifications, criteria and contractual requirements.

M   (d)   Maintain documentation for currently qualified personnel and processes according to the requirements of pertinent codes and standards.

O   (e)   Define the necessary qualifications of personnel and procedures for special processes not covered by existing codes or standards, or where item or service quality requirements exceed the requirements of established codes or standards.

O   (f)   Not consider concreting as a special process. However, the contractor shall ensure that foremen and vibration operators are properly selected from experienced or trained personnel prior to assignment of works and are given regular training by concrete placement experts.

3.2.13. Packaging and Shipping

Not applicable.

3.2.14. Quality Records

The contractor shall:

M   (a)   Maintain quality records as evidence that:

(i)   The quality assurance programme meets the requirements of these Quality Management Requirements (manual, procedures, quality plan).
(ii)   The items or services meet contractual or other applicable technical requirements (drawings, specifications, calculations, inspection and test procedures).

M   (b)   Maintain final performance quality records which include as appropriate:

(i)   as-built records
(ii)   material test reports or certificates
(iii)   non-destructive examination records or certificates
(iv)   inspection and test records
(v)   non-conformance reports.

Items (iii) and (iv) apply to those operations performed after receipt of material from the supplier.

M   (c)   Establish a procedure for 3.2.14.
O   (d)   Maintain quality records as evidence that

procurements meet the requirements of 3.2.3.

M   (e)   Maintain quality records as evidence that special processes are qualified as required by 3.2.12.(c).

O   (f)   Maintain quality records as evidence that measuring and test equipment are calibrated as required by 3.2.4.

O   (g)   Identify, index and file quality records for easy retrieval.

O   (h)   Retain quality records for the time specified in the contract. If not specified final performance quality records shall be retained for 10 years.

O   (i)   Provide for safe storing of records to minimize deterioration or damage and to prevent loss (the use of a double filing system is an acceptable method).

3.2.15. *Non-conformances*

The contractor is responsible for the identification and disposition of all non-conforming items, including those of subcontractors. Final acceptance of the contractor's disposition of those items that violate contractual requirements is the prerogative of the customer.

The contractor shall:

M   (a)   Establish and maintain measures for controlling non-conforming items that:

     (i)   Define the responsibility and authority of those who dispose of non-conforming items. This shall include provision for a technical review that involves those who are responsible for design, manufacturing, construction and quality functions, if these functions are concerned.

     (ii)   Detect and record non-conformances promptly except if corrected immediately in accordance with common construction practices.

     (iii)   Identify and hold non-conforming items for evaluation; these need not be held if subsequent work is not affected.

     (iv)   Develop a disposition that has the concurrence of all responsible parties.

     (v)   Implement the accepted disposition. This shall

include requirements for re-inspecting and retesting repaired and reworked items.

(vi) Verify the implementation of accepted dispositions.

M   (b) Establish a procedure for 3.2.15.

O   (c) Provide for holding areas or methods for segregating non-conforming items to prevent unauthorized use, shipment, or mixing with conforming items. However, where physical segregation is not practical or the non-conformance is not clearly visible, tagging, marking or other positive means of identification are acceptable.

M   (d) Maintain records identifying non-conforming items, the nature and extent of non-conformance, its disposition, and objective evidence that repaired and reworked items have been re-inspected or retested according to applicable procedures.

3.2.16. *Customer-supplied Items*

The customer is responsible for specifying in the contract the Quality Management Requirements applicable for items supplied by himself to the contractor and for certifying that these items are consistent with the quality requirements or the final work.

The contractor shall:

O   (a) Verify customer certification.

O   (b) Examine customer-supplied items on receipt for completeness and proper type and to detect transit damage. Further receiving inspection is not required unless the contractor needs actual characteristics for subsequent work or unless specified in the contract. Examination may be deferred until further processing is scheduled if items are in sealed containers or have special preservation or packaging.

O   (c) Control customer-supplied items from receipt onwards according to the requirements of this standard.

O   (d) Report promptly in writing to the quality assurance representative any customer-supplied items found damaged, lost, non-conforming, or otherwise unsuitable or unnecessary for use either on receipt or while in the contractor's custody.

O   (e)   Establish a procedure for 3.2.16.

4. VERIFICATION OF QUALITY

4.1. INITIAL EVALUATION

4.1.1. *Quality Assurance Programme, Facilities and Physical Resources*

O   Prior to the time of performing the works the customer shall evaluate the contractor's quality assurance programme, construction facilities and resources to determine whether the requirements of this chapter can be met.

In the event of the contractor not fulfilling all applicable requirements, the customer may award the contract provided that he takes the responsibility for those QA requirements that will not be met by the contractor. In such a case, the exceptions shall be clearly defined in the contract.

4.1.2. *Quality Plan*

M   The customer shall evaluate the quality plan and all revisions thereto in order to determine its acceptability.

The customer shall indicate his witness points on the accepted quality plan.

4.2. CONTINUING EVALUATION AND VERIFICATION

M   The customer shall perform surveillances according to the accepted quality plan.

4.3. ACCESS

M   The contractor shall provide for reasonable access of the competent authorities and of the customer to his premises and records for surveillance purposes.

5. ATTACHMENT: SUMMARY OF THE REQUIREMENTS

The following summary of the requirements is given as a checklist to determine the applicable requirements to be included in a contract. An optional requirement ( ) becomes mandatory when the space between the brackets is filled in with a cross (X).

Clause	Title of Clauses, Content	(X) = applicable ( ) = not applicable
3.	Requirements	
3.1.	Basic Requirements	
3.1.1.	Quality Assurance Programme	(X)
3.1.2.	Organization	
(a and b)	Management policies and representative for quality requirements	(X)
(c)	Personnel for inspections	( )
(d)	Organization chart	( )
(e and f)	Responsibility and authority	( )
3.1.3.	Quality Assurance Documents	
3.1.3.1.	Quality Assurance Manual	
(a and b)	Preparation, revision, implementation and content of the manual	(X)
(c)	Submission to the customer	( )
3.1.3.2.	Quality Plan	
(a and b)	Preparation, revision, submission, implementation and content	(X)
(c)	Quality plan for subcontracted items	( )
3.1.3.3.	Quality Assurance Procedures (General)	(X)
3.2.	Specific Requirements	
3.2.1.	Design Management (see D-Standards)	
3.2.2.	Document Control	

Clause	Title of Clauses, Content	(X) = applicable ( ) = not applicable
(a)	Approval of documents	(X)
(b and c)	List of document changes	( )
(d)	Design field changes	(X)
3.2.3.	Procurement	
3.2.3.1.	Selection of Subcontractors	
(a)	Activities and applicable requirements	(X)
(b and c)	Selection, evaluation	( )
3.2.3.2.	Subcontract Requirements	
(a–d)	Activities, applicable requirements, contractor's QA procedures, packaging, shipping	(X)
(e–i)	Rights of the owner and contractor's customer, additional requirements	( )
(j)	Approval	(X)
3.2.3.3.	Amendments to Subcontracts	(X)
3.2.3.4.	Verification of the Quality Management System Implemented by a Subcontractor (as required by the subcontract)	
3.2.3.5.	Receiving Inspection	
(a)	Inspection	(X)
(b)	Release of non-conforming incoming items	( )
3.2.4.	Measuring and Testing Equipment	
(a–c)	Evidence of valid measurements	(X)
(d–g)	Procedure, documentation	( )
3.2.5.	Inspection and Test	(X)
3.2.6.	In-process Inspection	
(a)	Inspection	(X)
(b–d)	Additional requirements	( )
3.2.7.	Final Inspection	
(a)	Inspection	(X)

Clause	Title of Clauses, Content	(X) = applicable ( ) = not applicable
(b and c)	Additional requirements	( )
3.2.8.	Inspection Status	
(a)	Inspection status	( )
(b)	Identification of non- conforming items	(X)
3.2.9.	Identification and Traceability	
(a–c)	General requirements	( )
(d)	Particular requirements for concreting	(X)
3.2.10.	Preservation, Handling and Storage	( )
3.2.11.	Construction	( )
3.2.12.	Special Processes	
(a and b)	List of special processes	(X)
(c)	Procedure for qualification	( )
(d)	Qualification records	(X)
(e and f)	Additional requirements	( )
3.2.13.	Packaging, Shipping (not applicable)	
3.2.14.	Quality Records	
(a–c)	Maintenance, content and procedure	(X)
(d)	Procurement records	( )
(e)	Special processes	(X)
(f)	Calibration	( )
(g–i)	Filing and storage	( )
3.2.15.	Non-conformances	
(a and b)	Control of non- conformance, procedure	(X)
(c)	Segregation	( )
(d)	Records	(X)
3.2.16.	Customer-supplied Items	( )
4.	Verification of Quality	
4.1.	Initial Evaluation	
4.1.1.	Quality Assurance Programme, Facilities and Physical Resources	( )
4.1.2.	Quality Plan	(X)

Clause	Title of Clauses, Content	(X) = applicable ( ) = not applicable
4.2.	Continuing Evaluation and Verification	(X)
4.3.	Access	(X)

Quality Management Requirements C3

Contents

1. SCOPE   146

1.1. General   146
1.2. Applicability   146
1.3. Contractor's Responsibilities   146

2. DEFINITIONS   146

3. REQUIREMENTS   146

3.1. Basic Requirements   146
3.2. Specific Requirements   147
3.2.1. Procurement   147
3.2.2. Measuring and Testing Equipment   147
3.2.3. Inspection and Test   147
3.2.4. Quality Records   147
3.2.5. Non-conformances   147

4. VERIFICATION OF QUALITY   148

4.1. Access   148

1. SCOPE

1.1. GENERAL

This chapter specifies requirements to be complied with by the contractor to ensure an efficient quality management in construction.

1.2. APPLICABILITY

The requirements of this chapter apply to construction activities when specified in a contract.

1.3. CONTRACTOR'S RESPONSIBILITIES

The contractor's responsibilities are:

(a)   To detect and dispose of non-conformances to contractual requirements.
(b)   To comply with the customer's requirements as specified in the contract.
(c)   To produce objective evidence that items meet contractual requirements.
(d)   To initiate corrective measures promptly when the quality assurance representative notifies the contractor of deviations from established requirements.

2. DEFINITIONS

Refer to Quality Management Directive.

3. REQUIREMENTS

3.1. BASIC REQUIREMENTS

Not applicable.

3.2. SPECIFIC REQUIREMENTS

3.2.1. Procurement

The contractor shall prepare subcontract documents that provide a clear description of the items or services to be procured including technical data and inspection and test requirements by reference to standards, technical specifications, drawings, etc.

The contract shall process amendments to subcontracts in the same way as the initial subcontract and reference the initial subcontract number in amendments.

The contractor shall identify and inspect items on receipt in a manner commensurate with their importance.

3.2.2. Measuring and Testing Equipment

No special calibration and control measures are necessary on rulers, tape measures, levels and other such devices, if normal commercial practices provide for adequate accuracy and/or if large tolerances are allowed for the corresponding measurements.

In all other cases, the contractor shall provide objective evidence that measuring and testing equipment can provide for valid measurements.

3.2.3. Inspection and Test

The contractor shall inspect and test the items as necessary and document the results.

3.2.4. Quality Records

The contractor shall establish and maintain inspection and test records.

3.2.5. Non-conformances

The contractor shall detect and dispose of all non-conforming items. Final acceptance of the contractor's disposition of those items that violate contractual requirements is the prerogative of the customer.

4. VERIFICATION OF QUALITY

4.1.   ACCESS

If specified in the contract, the contractor shall provide for reasonable access of the customer to his premises and records for surveillance purposes.